Sketch for a World-Picture

A STUDY OF EVOLUTION

Nebula in Andromeda, M.31 *(Photo from the Hale Observatories)*

Sketch for a World-Picture

A STUDY OF EVOLUTION

John Vyvyan

London
MICHAEL JOSEPH

First published in Great Britain by MICHAEL JOSEPH LTD
52 Bedford Square, London, W.C.1
1972

7181 0981 3

*Set and printed in Great Britain by Tonbridge Printers Ltd,
Peach Hall Works, Tonbridge, Kent, in Bell 11 on 12 pt.
and bound by James Burn at Esher, Surrey*

To

Nigel and Amanda

Contents

Illustrations

Acknowledgements

My thanks are due to the following for permission to quote from works in which they hold the copyright: George Allen & Unwin Ltd, for *Number: The Language of Science* by Tobias Dantzig; Cambridge University Press, for *Astronomy and Cosmology* by James Jeans, and *Plant Life Through The Ages* by A. C. Seward; Cassell & Co. Ltd, for *Wild Life in South Africa* by James Stevenson-Hamilton; University of Chicago Press, for *Man and The Vertebrates* by A. S. Romer; The Clarendon Press, for *The Structure of Physical Chemistry* by Sir Cyril N. Hinshelwood, and *The Measure of The Universe* by J. D. North; Collins Publishers, for *Before Nature Dies* by Jean Dorst, translated by Constance Sherman; The Hogarth Press, for *The Standard Edition of the Complete Psychological Works of Sigmund Freud*, revised and edited by James Strachey; McGraw-Hill Book Company, for *Principles of Paleaoecology* by D. V. Agar; Methuen & Co. Ltd, for *Supernormal Faculties in Man* by Eugene Osty, and *Learning and Instinct* by W. H. Thorpe; Thomas Nelson & Sons Ltd, for *Principles of Physical Geology* by Arthur Holmes; *Observer*, for 'Science and God' by Julian Huxley; Oliver and Boyd, for *Our Wandering Continents* by A. L. Du Toit, *The Morphology of The Earth* by Lester King, *The Origin of Life on Earth* by I. A. Oparin, and *Animal Dispersion in Relation to Social Behaviour* by V. C. Wynne-Edwards; Pergamon Press Ltd, for *The Problem of the Origin of Proteins* by F. Cedrangolo; and David Pilbeam, for 'Man's Earliest Ancestors', from *Science Journal*.

CHAPTER ONE

The Cosmic Setting

THE MYSTIC AND THE MATHEMATICIAN

We know nothing of an origin. We are the present, but transient outcome of a process of ceaseless change. *Tempora mutantur et nos mutamur in illis.* 'Impermanent are all component things.' This fact has been recognized often in the past, and it is the foundation of modern thought. If we look back on the process of becoming, towards an origin, in an attempt to understand why we are what we are, we find that everything grows gradually simpler. With the recession of time, brains and nervous systems become smaller and less complex, organisms dwindle into cells, the cells dissolve into molecules, the molecules into atoms, and the atoms into subatomic particles and waves. It would seem as if we were being led towards an ultimate simplicity. But this is a destination which our understanding cannot reach. It is utterly elusive, and we know no more about it than did the ancient Taoist sages. We dislike the bold paradox that they accepted, and we struggle to avoid it, but in the end it is inescapable.

> *The Way is like an empty vessel*
> *That yet may be drawn from*
> *Without ever needing to be filled.*

Those who have seen furthest into this seeming void, from which all things mysteriously emerge, are the mystic and the mathematician.

In mathematics, there is no symbol for 'perhaps'. And that is why all the sciences aim to be as mathematical as possible, just as all the arts, so it is said, aspire to the condition of music. When the scientist asserts, as he often does, 'I have found this to be true in all my observations, therefore it is a law,' someone may always murmur, 'Perhaps.' But when the mathematician has solved his equations, doubt is silenced. Or if doubt is not utterly silenced, the only person who is likely to go on quibbling will be a philosopher. There is consequently a general hankering after mathematics, and its primacy is undisputed.

How firm are the foundations of this belief?

Professor Dantzig has drawn an engaging picture of the mathematician as a fashion designer. Once upon a time (and this was a very long time ago) he began by making clothes for bodies. Then little by little he became entranced by his own creations, lost interest in bodies, and took to designing 'pure clothes'. If some body was afterwards discovered that could wear one of these garments, he was pleased; but in reality it was only of passing interest to him. The designer's true vocation had become *la couture idéale*.

The sciences, on the other hand, naked, shivering and ashamed, were all longing for a dress of magic numbers that would make them look respectable. The fit, however, was never perfect; for even in the realm of mathematical design there is a flaw. We cannot conceive the world without the contradictory intuitions of continuity and discontinuity, of line and number. The edge of any ruler exemplifies this paradox: it presents a line, and the most fundamental intuition that we have of a line is its continuity; it simultaneously presents numbered intervals, and the essence of our sense of number is discreteness.

A great part of the history of mathematics concerns the struggle with this problem – how to achieve a correspondence between lines and numbers, geometry and arithmetic, the continuous and the discrete. It cannot be done by rational numbers, and so infinite processes and irrational numbers insinuated themselves into the foundations of mathematical thought. Consider the number 1.999. . . The mind cannot impose a limit absolutely, a 'last number' cannot be conceived – in fact it can be proved that it does not exist – and so it will always be possible to add another 9. The mathematician can thus place an infinite numerical sequence between 1 and 2. It makes an infinitely close approach to 2, it may be said to represent 2, but it is not 2. Is this to give an arithmetical meaning to our intuition of continuity, or is it a confidence trick?

In any case, there is a discrepancy that cannot be avoided; and it was the attempt to relate line to number that first raised the problem, What is the square root of 2? This appears to be simple, but the search for the square root of 2 leads to a fraction that goes on for ever. Between $1\frac{1}{2}$, which is too much, and $1\frac{1}{4}$, which is too little, there is a mathematical infinity of numbers – and yet there is none that gives the answer. The fraction goes on and on, seeming to get nearer and nearer, but never arriving at the perfect answer. This phantom is an irrational number, and such mathematical beings can neither be comprehended nor expelled. Dantzig puts it in this way:

'The harmony of the universe knows only one musical form – the *legato*; while the symphony of number knows only its opposite – the *staccato*. All attempts to reconcile this discrepancy are based on the hope that an accelerated *staccato* may appear to our senses as a *legato*. Yet our intellect will always brand such attempts as deceptions and reject such theories as an insult, as a metaphysics that purports to explain away a concept by resolving it into its opposite. But these protests are in vain.'*

When the Pythagoreans discovered that some of the most fundamental of all relations, those between the sides of a square and its diagonal, and between the circumference of a circle and its diameter, lead to irrational and transcendental numbers, they were so shocked that they thought the Supreme Architect must have made a mistake, and that they had found a flaw in the structure of the universe. So, indeed, they had, if it is assumed that the universe ought to conform to a rational arithmetic. And in our own times, the discovery of the Principle of Uncertainty, and of the fact that some of the most elementary entities we know of behave as both particles and waves, has been hardly less distressing to the well-ordered mind. But infinite processes and irrational numbers permeate the 'exact' sciences no less relentlessly than wave-particles enter into physics.

The mathematician now weaves only his simpler materials from rational numbers. He has discovered or created irrational numbers, imaginary numbers, complex numbers, hypercomplex numbers, transcendental numbers and even more diaphanous fabrics to clothe the incorporeal world. In thus passing into nothingness like the Taoist sages, he has shown, as they did, that reason itself must have a stop; and that if it were possible for us to know the world 'as it really is', it would not be a purely rational understanding.

It appears to us that the universe arises out of nothing and expands into nowhere. It assuredly does nothing of the sort, but these terminal voids are the limits of our comprehension.

*Tobias Dantzig, *Number: The Language of Science*, 4th edn., Allen & Unwin 1962, p.169.

It is on this nescience that our science rests. From a fathomless source, it springs like a fountain – physics, chemistry, biology, psychology – to break into the shimmering spray of thought. It ceases in mystery at both extremities; but when we attempt to discern an origin, the first entities that become intelligible to us are the mathematician's pure designs.

MODELS

Anyone who has now reached middle-age will be able to recall that there have been several 'new universes' in the course of his lifetime; and in the present exuberant state of cosmology, he may well outlive several more. These models are 'pure clothes' designed by the mathematician. As mathematical creations, some of them are beautiful and some appear exotic; but none entirely fits the cosmic body we are able to observe. The hope is for a gradual convergence of theory and fact. Part of the evidence that must be accounted for is that the universe is evolving – in the sense that from the lightest of the elements, hydrogen, the heavier elements are continually being formed – and it appears also to be expanding. The three most notable models of recent times are the steady-state theory, the oscillating or cyclic theory, and the point-source theory.

In 1928 Sir James Jeans put forward a suggestion, not entirely without precedent, but which seemed startling from such an authority. 'The centres of the nebulae,' he surmised, 'are of the nature of "singular points" at which matter is poured into our universe from some other, and entirely extraneous spatial dimension, so that, to a denizen of our universe, they appear as points at which matter is being continually created.'* Some twenty years after this, a new version of 'continuous creation' was advanced by Bondi and Gold, and independently by Hoyle, in their steady-state theories. According to them, new hydrogen is constantly appearing in space; and this provides the primary material of the physical world and also causes its expansion. In its first version, which is now obsolete, no attempt was made to explain the origin of the hydrogen; but Hoyle has since emended his steady-state

*James Jeans, *Astronomy and Cosmology* Cambridge University Press 1928, p. 352.

theory in a way that does broach the problem of how the electrons and protons, of which hydrogen is composed, might have arisen.*

According to the oscillation or cyclic theory, the mass of the universe is such that the forces of expansion, which are paramount at present, will eventually be counteracted by the force of gravitation, which tends to draw all matter together, and the universe will then begin to contract. It will ultimately be reduced to a kind of fire-ball – immensely dense, intensely hot, and in which the atomic structure of matter will be destroyed. In this condition it will be unstable; the fire-ball will explode; a new phase of expansion will be initiated; and the first element to be reconstituted will be hydrogen from which the others will be rebuilt. The universe is thus thought of as oscillating or pulsating with a periodicity of about eighty thousand million years. One might call this the phoenix theory.

The point-source theory is similar in so far as it postulates the explosion of a 'primaeval atom' but it looks on this as a 'first event' not recurrent, and assumes that the consequent expansion will continue for ever.

All these options and some others remain open. But a backward glance at the long history of speculative cosmologies shows it to be strewn with theories that have proved to be untenable; the ability to frame theories in this field, however, has always exceeded the power to make the observations that could prove them to be right. Present-day speculations face the same prospect. And Professor North concludes his impressive work on the subject by saying, 'The individual theory of cosmology is neither true nor false: like any other scientific theory it is merely an instrument of what passes for understanding.'†

It should, moreover, be born in mind that such words as 'infinity', 'space' and 'universe' are ambiguous. The philosopher, the mathematician, and the layman all use them; but they do not necessarily mean the same things. To the philosopher usually and to the layman nearly always, the universe means everything that is; but the universe of the astronomer is the physical universe, that of the modern cosmologist is the 'universe of discourse', and neither is claimed to be the Whole.

*F. Hoyle, *Galaxies, Nuclei and Quasars*, Heinemann 1965, chapter 5.
†J. D. North, *The Measure of the Universe*, Clarendon Press 1965, p. 407.

EVE, COPERNICUS AND HUBBLE

Time was, perhaps, when the astronomer was hardly less innocent than Eve, summoned from sleep by the mystery and beauty of the night, and looking at the stars with the eyes of a poet:

Why sleep'st thou, Eve? now is the pleasant time,
The cool, the silent, save where silence yields
To the night-warbling bird, that now awake
Tunes sweetest his love-laboured song; now reigns
Full orbed the moon, and with more pleasing light
Shadowy sets off the face of things; in vain,
If none regard; heaven wakes with all his eyes,
Whom to regard but thee – ?

The Earth was then the centre of the universe. Eve was the soul of the Earth, and the stars looked down in admiration on her beauty. Wandering through the moonlit garden, she came to the Tree. It seemed even more alluring than by daylight. Then she found that she was not alone. Standing beside the Tree, and gazing at it steadfastly, was the Mathematician. To her horror, he picked the fruit, ate some of it himself, and offered some to her:

Taste this, and be henceforth among the gods,
Thyself a goddess, not to earth confined,
But sometimes in the air, as we –

The name of the mathematician was Copernicus; and by his satanic arithmetic, almost a hundred years before Gallileo invented the telescope, he had reduced the Earth to a mere planet. His promises to Eve were a deception. She had felt able to understand the stars as the admiring eyes of heaven, but their mathematics was too much for her. Even if she could have grasped it, the humiliating discovery that the stars had not the faintest interest in herself was beyond any intellectual compensation. It can hardly be denied that a deep human satisfaction was then lost – not only to Eve, but to the poet in us all. And yet, even in the realm of poetry, there has been an acquisition; and when the new knowledge has been

20

assimilated, it will surely stir the imagination to a new splendour.

The Copernican universe reduced the importance of the Earth, but it offered no affront to the stars. Those that could be seen with the naked eye, and with the early telescopes, remained the ultimate standard of grandeur and immensity. That this 'infinite' company might one day be compared with a tiny swarm of gnats would have seemed ridiculous. But one puzzling feature had long been noticed. In the constellation of Andromeda, the clear-sighted may discern, without any optical aid, a faintly luminous haze. As it looks like a small patch of mist, the Roman astronomers called it a nebula; but they could not explain it, and they did not think it was important. In the eighteenth century, William Herschel had an inkling of the truth, but his views were not accepted; and it was only in the 1920s, when Hubble studied this and other nebulosities through the hundred-inch telescope, that the new cosmic pattern was revealed beyond dispute. It then became evident that the nebula in Andromeda was another 'island universe', a family of perhaps a hundred thousand million stars, very similar to our own, but separated from us by two million light-years of starless space.

Further exploration has shown that such 'island universes', the galaxies, are innumerable. It is estimated that there are trillions within the range of existing telescopes; there is no possibility of their being counted. Some are spherical, some elliptical, and some spiral, some are larger and some smaller than our own. A photograph of the nebula in Andromeda, M 31,* which is almost a twin of ours, gives a fair impression of what our galaxy would look like if we could view it as a whole from a distance. It is like a disk in its general outline. It is composed of stars, and of interstellar clouds of hydrogen and dust. Many of its stars must have planetary systems; but these, of course, are undetectable to us. This material is arranged in arms, or streamers, which coil into a tight knot at the centre and gradually unwind into a diffuse fringe. The pattern is not unlike that of a whorled shell.

This picture enables us to imagine our own situation. The Sun is placed a long way from the centre of the galaxy, about two-thirds out on one of the spiral arms. The entire system is revolving, and it is this motion which keeps it from

*Frontispiece.

collapsing on itself. Our customary notions of the movements of the Earth – that it is spinning on its axis and in orbit round the Sun – have therefore to be extended; for the whole solar system is also travelling round the galactic centre at an estimated speed of two hundred and forty kilometres a second. One full revolution, which could be taken as the unit of galactic time, requires about two hundred million years; and since the beginning of the Palaeozoic Era, only three of these great circuits have been made.

When it was realized that such galaxies lie in every direction, to the limits of observability, our conception of the universe was changed. The familiar stars, which had seemed a symbol of the infinite, became only a small family in a countless population. And with the advent of a still larger telescope, and then of radio-telescopes, no ground whatever remained for a sense of self-importance. Galaxies vary greatly in size, and our own is of average dimensions. The Sun is also an average star; and if anything in this cosmic mystery can be considered commonplace, we must be so.

When Hubble analysed the light coming from the galaxies, he found that, compared with a local source of light, there was a displacement towards the red end of the spectrum. The fainter the source – and faintness is an indication of distance – the greater the displacement. The only satisfactory explanation of the 'red shift' that has yet been put forward is that the object emitting the light is rapidly receding. So came into being, in the 1920s, the concept of the expanding universe.

Distances of such magnitude play tricks with time. Light is like a courier, it takes time to travel, and the news it brings is always out of date. We see the Sun as it was eight and a half minutes ago, and the remotest discernible galaxies are thousands of millions of light-years away. This is perhaps the oddest part of the 'modern' universe: it has no observable present, we can see only the past. If the Andromeda galaxy had been destroyed before the emergence of man on Earth, we could not know that, and it would still be faintly glowing in the midnight sky. By a mere adjustment of the telescope, we can look not only at any place but at any epoch that we please. Up to the limits imposed by vision, we do not have to deduce, but merely to perceive this cosmic history. Our giant telescopes are the corridors of time.

THE EVOLUTION OF THE ELEMENTS

Energy might be described as a property of matter that produces certain effects. Theoretical physics takes these effects as axioms, is elegantly based on them, and explains physical phenomena in terms of them. If we go on to ask for a description of matter, however, we find we are thinking in a circle; and if the question is pressed, there is no answer. The evidence begins with a number of particles exhibiting energy that we have to accept as elementary. These elementary particles can be treated mathematically, because certain numbers – such as mass, radius, charge, spin – can be ascribed to them. This does not bring us to the limits of reality, but to the frontier of what we can explain.

One of these particles is the electron. We can hardly prevent ourselves from trying to picture it, although it is not really picturable. A free electron may be described as a tiny spherical cloud of negative electricity. It has a tenuous boundary within which it gradually thickens until it becomes dense to the point of impenetrability. It is always in rapid movement. But if it is 'caught' by a proton – which is a more massive particle bearing an equal and opposite charge – it cannot escape; the two enter into an active partnership, the electron circling round the proton; and this constitutes the lightest and simplest of the atoms – hydrogen.

Atoms have often been likened to a solar system, the positively charged nucleus representing a sun and the negatively charged electrons its planets; but this analogy cannot be pressed very far. In proportion to the size of its parts, there is more empty space in an atom than there is in a solar system; and its electrons cannot be pictured as planets, because besides being or behaving as particles, they also are or behave as waves. Their paths, therefore, are not simple orbits, but regions in which each can be located with varying degrees of probability, and are known as orbitals. As well as circling the proton, the electron tends also to envelop it and therefore to screen it from other electrical attractions; but it can never do this perfectly, and that is why atoms are able to combine. But there could be no such combinations, and therefore no chemistry, until the atoms themselves, the hundred or so different elements, had been evolved.

If there was ever a time when the universe consisted of pure hydrogen, then the subsequent evolution of the physical world would be comprehensible in its general outline. The hydrogen would have gathered into nebulae; condensations within the nebulae would have become stars; and in the furnaces of the stars, the heavier elements would have been forged. It all hangs on an 'if', and the 'if' depends on the cosmological theory that we happen to favour. Fortunately, however, there are also some facts.

It is certain that at the present time hydrogen is overwhelmingly more abundant than any other element in the universe; it is also certain that the stars are a product of evolution – they were not always there; and so it is a tempting supposition – but here we are beginning to speculate – that the galaxies were once nebulae of pure hydrogen, and that it was from this material that the first generation of stars condensed. If that was so, then the other elements were built up in an orderly manner. As the material of a proto-star is gradually compressed, by gravitation and other forces, the heat in the interior increases. When the temperature at the centre reaches about ten million degrees centigrade, the first nuclear reactions take place, and hydrogen begins to be converted into the second element, helium. One consequence of this is a sudden radiation of energy. This new energy, being released at the centre, tends to expansion, and it counteracts the gravitational energy which was causing the contraction. Eventually a balance is struck; and this balance, between two manifestations of energy, is the creation of a star.

We can understand this transmutation; because to a minute extent, in our hydrogen bombs, we can perform it. On a larger scale, we can observe it happening in the Sun. Inside the Sun, five hundred and sixty-four million tons of hydrogen are being transmuted, every second, into five hundred and sixty million tons of helium. Considered as matter, the difference of four million tons is annihilated; but in point of fact, it is being converted into energy and radiated into space. In this way, the Sun and the other stars will continue shining for a very long time; but it costs them something – they are losing mass every instant. This process explains more than radiation, for it reveals also the origin of the elements: they are created out of hydrogen in the centres of the stars.

It is not whole atoms, but only their nuclei that are formed in this manner. It is far too hot in the depths of a star for the attendant electrons to settle into their orbitals, and so to 'finish' the atoms in the form in which they exist on Earth. The stellar phase is one of nuclear creation, and this consists in the binding together of protons and neutrons. About a hundred other nuclear entities, inconceivably small and evanescent, are now known to exist, and it is expected that others will be found. This perplexing company, which somebody called the 'nuclear zoo', cannot be dismissed as unimportant, because it concerns the immensely powerful forces by which the nuclear particles are bound; but we shall not consider it here. The larger nucleons, which determine for each atom its number and its weight, are the protons and neutrons.

A neutron is slightly more massive than a proton, and, as its name implies, it is electrically neutral. It is able to change into a proton; and when it does so, it emits an electron and an anti-neutrino. In a sense, therefore, a neutron contains an electron or has the capacity to create one; but there are no independent electrons in an atomic nucleus. The reverse of this process is also possible: a proton and an electron can change into a neutron and a neutrino. Energy is needed to make this happen; but as there is plenty of heat energy in the centre of a star, neutrons will always be available there for nuclear creation.

The helium nucleus is made up of two protons and two neutrons. Its atomic number is therefore two, because only the protons are counted for this; but its atomic weight is a little over four, since all the constituents are included in the weight. The heavier nuclei are also a mixture of protons and neutrons, not always in equal parts, and are classified in the same way – by number and by weight.

The jump from the one proton of hydrogen to the four nucleons of helium is made possible by stepping-stones. Although every atom of a given element has the same number of protons, all do not have the same number of neutrons – the atomic number for each is constant, but the atomic weight is not. There are forms of hydrogen – heavy hydrogen, H^2 and H^3 – which contain one proton and either one or two neutrons;

and there is a form of helium – He³ – which contains only one neutron. These act as bridges between the usual forms of the elements. The sequence in which the lighter nuclei are built up in the stars will be seen most clearly in a diagram. The symbols printed below in heavy black represent successive additions to nuclei that have already been formed, and the figures stand for the sum of their protons and neutrons.

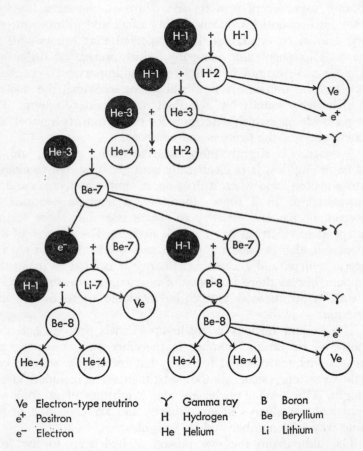

Ve	Electron-type neutrino	Ɣ	Gamma ray	B	Boron
e⁺	Positron	H	Hydrogen	Be	Beryllium
e⁻	Electron	He	Helium	Li	Lithium

The Sun is a second generation star; and although it is transmuting hydrogen at the present time, it has always contained many other elements that it did not itself create. As it is not a very big star, it will never be able to generate sufficient heat by gravitational compression to forge the heaviest nuclei. Its present interior temperature is about fifteen million degrees. To finish the work of nuclear creation is the labour of the giants, in which temperatures of more than a hundred million degrees may be attained. Stars of this magnitude consume their hydrogen quickly. When it is exhausted, the release of energy from the centre ceases; gravitation is then unopposed, and the star begins to shrink. It consequently grows hotter; and the temperature continues to rise until a new cycle of transmutation based on helium is set up, and eventually a new balance of energy is struck.

By this process, nuclei up to the iron group are forged. The iron nucleus is the most tightly bound of all. That is why iron is such a common element, and why the principles of construction are different for nuclei that are heavier than iron. The formation of these does not depend on higher temperatures, but on unusual encounters; and consequently none of them is common, and some are very rare. There is a limit to the size of stable nuclei, beyond which they break up spontaneously: these are the radioactive elements. Some of them disintegrate at once; but others, like uranium, have a long life-span, and these have been immensely important in the history of the Earth.

STAR-DUST

From the point of view of life, the labour of the stars would have been fruitless if they had kept their newly-forged elements within themselves. The majority, of course, do this – but not all. Until the invention of the radio-telescope, it was impossible to map our own galaxy in detail, because it contains, as many others are known to do, immense clouds of dust. These are impenetrable to a light-telescope, and obscure its view of many regions. It is from this material, at least in part, that stars of the second and third generation and their attendant planets form. Indeed, it contains all the elements that are necessary to life, and the potentiality of such beings as ourselves. Where did these cosmic dust-clouds come from?

There is a class of star that scatters a part of its substance into space, almost as a plant casts its ripe seeds to the wind. These are the exploding stars, the supernovae. They are always giants; and it is precisely in this type of star that the full range of nuclear creation will already have been achieved.

There are critical conditions of mass and temperature that cause a star to explode; and it is estimated that one does so in our own galaxy about once in every eighty years. Several have been observed; a faint or previously invisible star will suddenly, and for a short time, assume intense brilliance, and may even outshine all other objects in the night-sky. Such an event was recorded by the Chinese astronomers in 1054; the remnants of this explosion can still be seen rapidly expanding, and they have been photographed through the 200-inch telescope at Mount Palomar. The chance that any part of this material will ever be incorporated in a life-bearing planet is, of course, remote; and yet the chance exists, for the nucleus of every atom in our bodies was forged in some departed giant, far greater than the Sun, and then scattered into space in such a cosmic cloud. It is from the dust of the stars that we have been assembled.

The Sun, as has been said, is a second generation star. It is mainly composed of hydrogen, but it also incorporated at the time of its formation vast quantities of interstellar dust. It may be that the planets as a whole consist of the same material – of the part that was left over at the time of the solar birth; and that the elements, which are not distributed in the same proportions in all the planets, were sorted out, as it were, when the chain was in process of formation.

There is, however, an alternative to this: the Sun may at first have been a solitary star, which encountered and then organized into planets a dense cloud of interstellar dust. Of the numerous theories of planetary formation that have been advanced from time to time, these two are the only survivors: unremitting mathematical and observational testing has gradually eliminated all the rest. From either theory, there follow two important consequences, both of which run counter to earlier assumptions, but which are now generally accepted. One is that planetary systems cannot be uncommon; and although they are not observable at such great distances, millions of stars must be attended by planets, and there will be many that resemble the Earth. The other is that the Earth did not originate as a globe of incandescent gas, but was at first a cold body, formed by the accretion of particles in the proto-planetary cloud.

It is not necessary to invoke any other principles than these in order to understand how the heavier elements are formed and scattered, and why some of them are scarce and others abundant. But that is not to say that the supernovae are the only crucibles in nature in which they might have been made. In addition to exploding stars there may also be exploding galaxies. Our own galaxy is a rather peaceful place; but there are others, some of them among the most distant objects that can be observed, which are now known to be releasing energy on a scale quite outside our experience – at the rate of about 10^{45} ergs per second. To maintain this requires the annihilation, second by second, of a mass equal to hundreds of millions of Suns. The nuclear transformations that we understand are too feeble to account for it; and gravitational collapse and the mutual destruction of matter and anti-matter are among the explanations that have been suggested. It may be that our supernovae are only little smithies, and that there are foundries in the universe where the elements are mass-produced. But these are questions on which we can still only speculate, and our local blacksmiths would have been sufficient for our needs.

ATOMIC SHELLS AND CHEMICAL BONDS

In the depths of a supernova, where even the atoms are unfinished, there can, of course, be no chemical compounds; but in the proto-planetary dust-cloud there were many. Somewhere in space, on the fringe of the stars, chemistry is born. Chemistry takes the nuclei for granted, because the nuclear components are too tightly bound together to be affected by anything that normally happens to them outside the stars. Its field is the next great phase of world-synthesis – the interactions between atomic shells. Before chemistry can begin, the electrons must have settled down in their orbitals. And when they have done so, their dispositions fundamentally determine nearly everything else.

'In general it can be said that the picture of the world with the tough fibres of its woods, the laminae of its rocks, the elastic tissues of its living beings, its burnished and resonant metals, its hard diamonds, and its friable salts can be referred back to a fundamental motif of which it is only an elaboration.'*

*C. N. Hinshelwood, *The Structure of Physical Chemistry*, Oxford 1951, p. 317.

This underlying motif is the laws that govern the placing of the electrons around the nuclei. When this is understood, Sir Cyril Hinshelwood adds, 'The spectacle of nature may seem more uniform: it hardly seems less mysterious.' These laws are fundamental because it is due to the configuration of their shells that the atoms are able to combine and so to build the patterns of a substantial world. If they could not combine, everything would remain in the state of a gas – a chaotic concourse of separate particles.

When the temperature is very high, the electrons are uncontrollable; but when it is sufficiently reduced, each nucleus attracts and retains the same number of electrons as it has of protons; the positive and negative charges are then balanced, the atom is electrically neutral, and it may be said to be 'finished'. This settles the numerical problem very simply, but the exact placing of these satellites is a more complicated matter. Once again, 'pictures' based on experience of the familiar world fail. In addition to its wave-like nature, an electron has a property called spin; and the imagination cannot create a 'picture' that will reconcile the concepts of particle, wave and spin. It is mathematically demonstrable, however, and must be accepted as a fundamental fact, that one orbital will accommodate two electrons of opposite spin – never more than two and never two that have the same spin. If a third electron is attracted and 'caught', it will have to move in a new orbital further out; and in this position it will be less tightly bound. It is on this principle, from inside outwards, orbital by orbital, that the atoms build their shells.

The single electron of a hydrogen atom cannot screen its nucleus perfectly, and this accordingly retains some ability to attract: the atom as a whole has, therefore, an inclination to combine with others. In contrast to this, the two electrons of the helium atom completely fill the first orbital; the balance is perfect; the nucleus can exert no influence beyond this electric shell; and helium is consequently the first of the so-called 'noble gasses' – it is entirely self-satisfied and enters into no chemical compounds at all. However complicated intra-atomic relationships may become, this quest for perfect symmetry remains the secret of everything they do.

The filled orbital of helium constitutes the first shell. It is unique in its simplicity; and all the other shells, which build up round it, consist of a group of orbitals. There are four orbitals in the second shell. To complete this requires eight electrons; and eight has been called the 'magic number', because when it is reached, a perfect balance is again achieved. A shell may be said to be finished, closed, when it contains an octet. Beginning with 2, therefore, shells are completed at atomic numbers 10 and 18. These are the elements neon and argon; and like helium they are both noble gasses, and do not react with anything. All the elements between them are reactive, their affinities depending on the number of electrons in the un-finished outer shell. This number – known as their valence number – discloses in advance how they are likely to behave; because the object of their combining is always to build a complete outer shell in association – to form an octet together.

The discovery of this principle is surely one of the most satisfying that the human mind has ever made; because it provides a fundamental explanation of why all the substances by which we are surrounded, and of which we are composed, are as they are and behave as they do. The structure of the larger shells is more complex, but the principle remains the same: it is the search for perfect stability.

Although this book is not intended to be a text-book, a table of the first twenty elements is included here as an illu-stration. The figures on the left stand for the number of protons in the nucleus – the atomic number. Those on the right stand for the number of electrons in successive shells. Italics indicates that the outer shell is incomplete – these are the valence numbers.

Protons			Electrons	
1	Hydrogen	H	*1*	
2	Helium	He	2	
3	Lithium	Li	2	*1*
4	Beryllium	Be	2	*2*
5	Boron	B	2	*3*
6	Carbon	C	2	*4*
7	Nitrogen	N	2	*5*
8	Oxygen	O	2	*6*
9	Fluorine	F	2	*7*
10	Neon	Ne	2	8

Protons			Electrons			
11	Sodium	Na	2	8	*1*	
12	Magnesium	Mg	2	8	*2*	
13	Aluminium	Al	2	8	*3*	
14	Silicon	Si	2	8	*4*	
15	Phosphorus	P	2	8	*5*	
16	Sulphur	S	2	8	*6*	
17	Chlorine	Cl	2	8	7	
18	Argon	A	2	8	8	
19	Potassium	K	2	8	8	*1*
20	Calcium	Ca	2	8	8	*2*
	etc.					

As the purpose for which atoms combine is to form an octet together, elements that have one electron in their outer shell and those that have seven are predestined partners. These unite in a distinctive way which gives rise to a crystalline structure. The atoms with only one electron lose it rather easily, while those with seven have a facility for picking it up – or they might be said to steal it. As a result of this theft, both are left with an outer shell of eight; but they have not achieved the poise of the noble gases, because they have become electrically unbalanced. An atom in this state is termed an ion.

When ions are oppositely charged, they attract one another. They arrange themselves alternately, positive to negative, building a kind of honeycomb; and since the outer shell of each is perfectly symmetrical, the resulting structure is a crystal. The union of one with seven is the most obvious example of this kind of association; but atoms with other valence numbers can become ions, and being of different sizes, they can build a great variety of crystalline forms. All crystals are alike however, in the smoothness of their surfaces, the regularity of their angles, and their transparency; and these properties are due to the special way in which their atoms are held together. This is the ionic bond.

The metals are also composed of ions. They differ from crystals, however, because their ions are all positive; and they would fly apart, if it were not that the 'lost' electrons, which formerly belonged to the incomplete shells, are held in common by the entire group. The ions in a metal are like islands or ships on an electric sea, and a current in this sea is an electric current. The strikingly different properties of crystals and metals are thus seen to derive from the bonding of their atoms: the metallic bond creates substances that are resonant, malleable, and conductors of electricity.

One other type of bonding must be mentioned here; because from the point of view of life, it is by far the most important – this is the covalent bond. In covalent compounds a few electrons – as many as are needed by each atom to complete its own octet – are shared between close neighbours; and it is this joint interest that holds them together and constitutes the covalent bond.

It will be noticed that at this point a new building-block has appeared in nature – the molecule. This is the primary unit of a compound; and if the molecule is split the unique properties of the compound disappear. On account of the intimate sharing of electrons in covalent bonding, the outer shells of the participating atoms interpenetrate, and so the resulting molecules may have an almost infinite variety of shape. Elements that stand midway between the noble gases, such as carbon and silicon, have a great ability to form covalent bonds. There are many more compounds of carbon than of all the other elements put together; and this marvellous versatility of the carbon atom is one of the chief prerequisites of life.

The chemistry of carbon is a science in itself; and even its simplest compounds, those made with hydrogen, become extremely complicated. These are the hydrocarbons, and their structure and behaviour afford a first insight into the chemistry of living things. The simplest of them is methane. To form a molecule of methane, one atom of carbon unites with four of hydrogen. By sharing electrons in this way, each of the hydrogen atoms obtains a closed shell like helium, while the carbon atom gains an octet. A diagram of the methane molecule, in which electrons are represented by dots, will illustrate this:

It would not be too fanciful, perhaps, to take this as a chemical symbol of the promise of life; because these structural principles permit limitless extension and complexity. Carbon atoms are able to link directly with one another, and this makes possible the giant molecules that are necessary to biochemistry. The possibilities are almost infinite; but three structural themes – long-chain molecules, branching chains, and rings – will give a hint of them.

```
    H           H  H          H  H  H          H  H  H          H
    |           |  |          |  |  |          |  |  |          |
H—C—H       H—C—C—H      H—C—C—C—H      H—C—C—C—·····—C—H
    |           |  |          |  |  |          |  |  |          |
    H           H  H          H  H  H          H  H  H          H


            H  H  H  H  H  H
            |  |  |  |  |  |
        H—C—C—C—C—C—C—H
            |  |  |  |
            H  |  H  H  |
               |        |
            H—C—H    H—C—H
               |        |
               H        H


                    H
                    |
               H    C    H
                \  ‖   \ /
              H—C      C—H
                 |     ‖
              H—C      C
                / \   / \
               H   C     H
                   ‖
                   C
                   |
                   H
```

The electrons are not represented in these formulae, but it is on their precise positions that every pattern hangs. And it will therefore be appreciated that the laws that determine the play of the electrons in their orbitals underlie and elucidate all the phenomena of the Earth, from its metallic-electric centre and its mantle of crystalline rocks to the most delicate fabric of its living forms.

Within the atoms and between the molecules there is space – space that is vast in proportion to the size of the particles that move within it. Whether between atom and atom, or between molecule and molecule, the forces that reach across these inner spaces and hold everything together vary in their strength. Some bonds are broken easily, others only by the exertion of tremendous energy; and this permits, among other things, variety of state.

Even in a solid, the molecules move, but only to vibrate about a fixed centre; if more energy is imparted to them in the form of heat, their vibrations increase in amplitude, the bonds come under strain, the substance expands and begins to melt; and if the temperature is raised sufficiently, the links are broken, and the molecules or atoms fly apart and become a vapour. In a solid the particles vibrate, in a liquid they glide, and in a gas they dart about; but at exactly what temperature these changes will occur in any particular substance depends on the strength of its bonds. If it were possible to reproduce the temperatures of the stars, the molecules would break up, the atomic shells would fly asunder, and only the nuclei, around which the whole manifestation of our more gentle Earth is gathered, would remain in the furnace where they were originally forged.

In describing this phase of evolution, one is liable to use the passive mood and to speak of these structures as having been shaped or formed or created. This is really a misconception. Protons and electrons are not arranged by some extraneous agency; they arrange themselves, and their relationships express their constitutions. The whole world-pattern is accordingly determined by the intrinsic nature of its constituent parts. It is not a design made out of passive materials, but a concrescence of active entities. Those that constitute the units of our visible, tangible world are the hundred or so varieties of atom; but the substratum on which they rest, or from which they arise, does not consist of small-scale models of large familiar things. We have no sensory experience of it at all, and we can find no analogies by which it could be represented in imagination.

GEOPOETRY

A little more than three centuries ago, in 1650, Archbishop Usher calculated that the creation of the world had been finished on the evening of 22nd October, 4004 B.C. He was merely putting a fine point on a chronology that had been accepted in Europe throughout the Christian era, and that not a few people still clung to even in the nineteenth century. Contemporary estimates of the age of the Earth would multiply this figure by more than a million. Some five thousand million years ago, it is now thought, the planets were in process of formation; and their age, as finished products, must be at least four thousand five hundred million years.

These figures have been arrived at by the study of meteorites and of the changes due to the decay of radioactive elements that have taken place in them. The rate of these changes is a constant, and provides a most important timepiece for pre-geological history. Rock specimens from the moon, however, suggest that the estimates based on them may still be too short. Unfortunately, we cannot calculate the birthday of our planet with the fine precision of the Archbishop. We have to admit a margin of error of a few hundred million years, but 5,000,000,000 B.P. (before present) is a fair approximation.

The knowledge on which this assessment rests is recent, and scientific myths of the Earth's formation have been hardly less plentiful than the religious myths of its creation. The one kind may be termed theories and the other doctrines; but both are myths in the sense that they are attempts to explain something that is known in terms of something that is not known – in short, by telling a story. When many minds have been at work on these stories, some of them will become splendid epic poems; and as such they will be worthy of remembrance, even when they ought no longer to be believed. The point at which astronomy and geology meet – the formative period of the Earth – has not quite emerged from mythology; because some fundamentally important facts are still unknown, and this leaves a place for the imagination.

Any picture that is presented by modern theory, however, is different from the one that has been so often painted and has become generally familiar. Until recently it was supposed that the Earth had once been a globe of incandescent gas, which slowly cooled to a molten state. For aeons, so it was thought, its surface was then swept by tides of fire, until some parts of it consolidated and became the nuclei of continents. This account has now been relegated to what Umgrove has aptly called the realm of geopoetry. It would be a pity to forget it, for it has an epic grandeur; and it is well to remember that science, like art and religion, has its splendid phantasies.

According to the new picture, the Earth grew by the accretion of solid particles in the proto-planetary cloud. The rate at which this took place is one of the points of uncertainty, and therefore the original temperature of the Earth is unknown. If the accumulation was rapid, the heat generated by the infalling particles would not have had time to disperse, and the Earth might have originated in a liquid state; but if the rate of formation was slow, this heat would have been lost, and the planet would have been initially cool and solid. Both these alternatives have eminent supporters, and both have been advanced with some assurance. But the balance of opinion appears to favour a rather slow rate of accumulation; and this suggests that the new-born Earth had only a moderate amount of heat, and was perhaps more nearly cold and solid than it ever has been since. There were no earthquakes, no volcanism, no surface water. The oceans and the atmosphere were still bound in the body of the Earth.

This view is made tenable by recent knowledge of radioactivity. Any theory, of course, must account for the fact that the Earth's interior is very hot at present, and that even its outer shells of basalt and granite were at one time molten. The heating can now be understood as due to the decay of radioactive elements; and a most important part of the new conception, therefore, is intense radioactivity in the young planet. It might, in fact, be said that the physical manifestations of the Earth have depended mainly on the constitution of a few heavy elements, while its biological activities depend on the nature of a few light ones.

We may accordingly imagine that in a planet that was at first homogeneous, solid throughout, and only moderately hot, radioactive elements were imprisoned; their spontaneous disintegration gave off more heat, and also brought about chemical changes in the substances around them. These events mounted to a climax, and then gradually subsided. The highest temperature was probably reached in less than a thousand million years – perhaps much less; and at that time, the Earth may have been molten or nearly so. The cooling that followed was at first rapid, then imperceptible, and at present it is thought that rather more heat is being generated in the interior than is lost at the surface.

Since the interior is not open to inspection, its present state and constitution have to be inferred from evidence of various kinds – the Earth's mass, its moment of inertia, the variations of its magnetic field and the behaviour of earthquake waves. These show that there are discontinuities of phase and substance between the crust and the mantle, and between the mantle and the core. So we are led to conjecture a metallic core, mainly of iron; a silicate mantle, which is not molten but hot enough to be plastic; and a relatively-brittle, solid crust, which is about thirty miles thick under the continents but less beneath the oceans. Direct observation, of course, is confined to the crust; but it is the forces from the depths, especially from the mantle, that maintain its perpetual unrest.

If the Earth was built up by the accretion of solid particles, the distribution of the elements within it must at first have been uniform. At present, this is far from being the case; and so any theory must account for their segregation. Although the Earth may seem to us a symbol of stability, incessant transformation is no less its characteristic. This is not merely superficial. From the core to the atmosphere there is motion and change, and the rate at which they occur depends mainly on the temperature. It is a moot point whether this was ever high enough to liquify the whole planet, but at least the melting point of iron must have been reached at a depth of a few hundred kilometres within a period of a few hundred million years. After that, the first differentiation of its substance would have taken place fairly quickly.

Four elements – iron, oxygen, magnesium and silicon – together make up more than nine-tenths of the Earth's mass. This overwhelming preponderance means that it was their behaviour which mainly determined the course of events – and especially the behaviour of iron and silicon. The one heavy, the other light, and both of them abundant, these were the first to become segregated; and there were formed in consequence an iron core and a mantle of silicates. This was the primary geochemical differentiation. It was brought about by gravity – the heavier phases sinking towards the centre and the lighter rising towards the surface. The wanderings and eventual settlement of the other and far scarcer elements were not determined so much by their weight as by their chemical affinity for iron or silicon; and one may therefore understand why some very heavy elements – such as uranium and thorium –

have migrated to the crust, and why it is likely that those that alloy readily with iron – such as gold and platinum – are concentrated in the inaccessible metallic centre.

Even if the whole surface was not molten when the temperature was highest, it must frequently have been inundated by vast irruptions of igneous rock. Heat was thus liberated, radioactivity began to decline, and the Earth became cooler. It was during this period that the lithosphere, the Earth's rocky envelope began to form. The primordial silicate melt, containing the mixed elements of both mantle and crust, commenced to solidify. As it slowly passed from the liquid into the crystal phase, it separated into layers. This is the secondary geochemical differentiation, which created the series of igneous rocks. Laboratory experiments have shown that from an original melt of the presumed composition, olivine crystals would be the first to form. It is accordingly supposed that the mantle originated as an accumulation of olivine crystals. When these were precipitated, the remaining liquid would have the general composition of a basalt, which would have been the next phase to solidify. This explains why the lowest layer of the crust, which immediately overlies the mantle, is now a world-encircling shell, some five kilometres thick, of basaltic rock. The last phase would have yielded a granite. Granite is the foundation of the continents and overlies the basalt wherever there is land. It does not, however, form a complete Earth-shell, and is absent, or nearly so, in the ocean basins. As granite is lighter than basalt, one may understand the general tendency of the continents to rise and the ocean floors to sink; and the process we have outlined affords an explanation of the first series of igneous rocks, over which a thin and tattered coat of the familiar sedimentary rocks has since been thrown.

More was thus created than these solid, surface features: a vast quantity of gases and water, previously bound, was given vent. The gases were mainly methane, ammonia, and carbon dioxide, and out of them an atmosphere was formed. This bore no resemblance to the air that now exists, and would have been lethal to present forms of life; but it was of critical importance to life's origin. The water was emitted as steam, which hung in clouds or gathered into pools where the rocks had cooled sufficiently. In course of time, as the temperature fell, the pools widened into lakes, the lakes into shallow seas, and the seas into oceans. The ceaseless round of rising vapour and falling rain began. The primordial rocks were gradually eroded, and the first sedimentary rocks were laid.

Such is the modern myth of the Earth's first thousand million years. Part of it is certainly true, and part of it is speculative. Until the question of temperature is answered – if it ever can be – there will be a place for geopoetry. The poem will relate that about five thousand million years ago the Earth had attained the status of a planet. It was spinning on its axis, and in orbit round the Sun; there was morning and evening, seasonal change, and a night-sky patterned with stars. It was homogeneous; there was no division into core, mantle and crust; there was neither sea nor air; and it was almost quiet to the depths. Within its body there was a scattering of unstable elements – uranium, thorium, potassium; and the transmutation of these, during an era of intense radioactivity, is the opening of the world-drama. The globe began to liquify and to undergo a primary differentiation of its elements. Iron, nickel and gold gathered in its metallic centre; silicon, magnesium, aluminium and most of the oxygen formed an encircling shell; and the less-abundant elements were segregated according to their affinities. As the pent-up energy was gradually expended and the radiogenic elements became fewer, the temperature began to fall, the first crystalline rocks to solidify, and the foundations of the lithosphere were laid – an Earth-shell of basalt supporting granite. By 3,000,000,000 B.P., or even earlier, the Earth had a covering of rocks or lithosphere, an expanse of surface waters or hydrosphere, and an atmosphere. It was still lifeless, but it was preparing to live.

CHAPTER TWO

Life

THE BRIDGE

The Earth is not merely a setting for life: it lives. We have seen its substance differentiate into lithosphere, hydrosphere and atmosphere; and so, in natural sequence, a biosphere arose. The biosphere is that portion of the Earth that is alive.

What is life? To begin with, it is a chemical process. Beyond that, no definition is yet agreed; but living things have familiar characteristics by which we easily distinguish them from rocks and air. They are able to maintain and to reproduce themselves; they can select from their environment those elements that are good for them, and reject those that are hurtful; they possess something which, at the simplest, is termed irritability, and which is the first hint of sentience; and in due time they come to know what they want and what they do not want to experience or to incorporate. Probably the most striking of these characteristics are reproducibility and sentience. Both seem to be far removed from the events we have been discussing; and to approach them, we must find a bridge – a bridge between geochemistry and biochemistry.

It may be as well, at this point, to assure readers who dislike any form of chemistry that there will be only a little of it in this book and that no previous knowledge will be assumed. There is, however, no way of evading the implications of our first definition of life – that it is a chemical process; and without some reference to chemistry, there can be no hope of understanding how this process, marvellous but not miraculous, arose. This is the bridge that we have to cross.

Once it has been appreciated that life is or arises from a chemical process, it no longer seems strange that there should be no real frontier in nature between the living and the non-living. One of the dubious forms of life, a virus, may exist in either a crystalline state or as a self-copying organism. In fact it is able to cross and re-cross the threshold of what we conventionally call life; and although it may be convenient to locate this threshold, to do so is somewhat arbitrary. A living organism is not essentially different from its environment: it is composed of the same elements and comes from the same unfathomable source. It is the pattern of form and function that

43

is different, but not the substance out of which the pattern is composed.

Since we live in the 'machine age' and tend to think in mechanical terms, it may be as well to make the point that even the simplest of living things is not, in the proper meaning of the word, a machine. A machine is a contrivance made for the contriver's use: a living body is a process maintaining itself, reproducing itself, and existing for itself. The outlooks of the engineer and the biochemist are therefore different: the one sees component parts as things to be put together and made to work, while the other sees them as things that put themselves together and work spontaneously. When the appropriate atoms or molecules meet in the right states of energy, they combine into electro-chemical systems in which chains of reaction are set up which constitute a living process. They are acting according to their nature; and we cannot conceive the universe and this life within it as something that is made arbitrarily, as a machine is made. It is a product of self-synthesis and an expression of its own self-nature.

It is by the laws of chance that the simpler components meet in the first instance, and so have the opportunity to exhibit their intrinsic properties in relation to one another; and since the world is in ceaseless motion, there will be an infinite number of such meetings. Associations that prove stable persist, those that are not fall apart. The stable aggregates then form the growing-points of more complex systems; but however elaborate these may become, each particle within them will have found its own place according to its affinities – it will be where it 'wants' to be.

Life, as we know it on this planet at this time, does not exhaust the possibilities of biochemistry. The characteristics that we term vital might have been based – and in other parts of the universe they probably are based – on a different combination of elements and reactions. The organic world of which we form a part is a special instance. To say that this or that is essential to life is to speak relatively, and may be true in our context only; but it is remarkable that the so-called essentials have not changed – they have merely been added to – since the first living cells appeared as the culminating product of geochemistry. Cells built of the same components and according to the same principles are the structural units of every larger organism with which we are acquainted. How and when did they first arise?

Volcanism, expanding surface waters, and an atmosphere that was different from the present one made the environment in which systems not yet living, but on the threshold of vitality, began to form. A number of elements played a role in this; but carbon and nitrogen were the leading actors, with hydrogen and oxygen, one might say, in supporting parts. Compounds of all of these were present in the Earth's primeval atmosphere. It had then no free oxygen; its free hydrogen was being rapidly lost; and methane, ammonia, water-vapour and probably carbon dioxide were its most important constituents. Some of these compounds probably existed in the proto-planetary cloud; but the oceans and the atmosphere were both once bound in the crust of the Earth and may be looked on as its exhalations. They were emitted during periods of intense volcanism, and have been slowly changing in quantity and constitution. The primeval atmosphere was rich in three compounds of vital significance, methane, ammonia, and water-vapour –

$$
\begin{array}{ccc}
\text{H} & \text{H} & \text{H} \\
| & | & | \\
\text{H—C—H} & \text{N—H} & \text{O—H} \\
| & | & \\
\text{H} & \text{H} &
\end{array}
$$

This mixture may look unpromising, and it would be deadly to the forms of life that exist now; but it is a first segregation of the vital elements. In methane, the carbon atom has completed its octet by combining with four hydrogen atoms; in ammonia, the nitrogen atom, which has five valence electrons, has achieved stability by union with three hydrogen atoms; and in water-vapour, oxygen, valency six, is satisfied with two. The elemental constituents of life – carbon, nitrogen, hydrogen and oxygen – bound into simple compounds by their intrinsic properties, were accordingly 'in the air' of the primeval world. And the secret of the origin of life lies in building out of this simplicity the marvellous configurations of biochemistry.

THE COMPOUNDS OF LIFE

Living cells are composed of protoplasm. This is chiefly water, holding in suspension a complicated mixture of chemical compounds. If it were possible to describe the evolution of protoplasm in detail, the task might be hardly less demanding than to trace the evolution of the nebulae. We shall not enter this labyrinth, but seek an insight into its nature by considering its two most important contents – proteins and nucleic acids. At present, both of these are assembled and put together within the living organism; but there was a time when the opposite was taking place, and living bodies were being built by them. This is the problem with which we are confronted – to understand how these compounds arose in the non-living world and then entered into vital association. Proteins are the building-blocks of all living things, but they themselves are built out of simpler units – the amino acids. It is accordingly to them that we must first look:

*'The problem of the origin of life is in the first place the problem of the origin and appearance of the amino acids on Earth; and in the second place, the problem of the mechanism by which the amino acids are combined to build the protein macromolecule.'**

What is an amino acid?

More than eighty are known to exist, and there are doubtless more; but only twenty or so are important in protein structure. The simplest of them is glycine, and glycine forms the foundation of all others. The glycine molecule is built round a central carbon atom –

C

to which is added an amino group NH_2 –

H
 \
  N–C
 /
H

---

*F. Cedrangolo, 'The Problem of the Origin of Proteins', in the International Union of Biochemistry Symposium Series, vol. I, *The Origin of Life on Earth*, Pergamon Press 1957, p. 281.

and an acid group COOH –

$$\begin{array}{c} H \\ | \\ H-N-C-C \end{array} \begin{array}{c} O \\ \\ OH \end{array}$$

and two hydrogen atoms –

$$\begin{array}{ccc} H & H & O \\ | & | & \\ H-N-C-C & \\ | & | & OH \\ H & H \end{array}$$

This formula can be written in various ways, and a molecule has, of course, no top or bottom; but we have spoken figuratively of glycine as a foundation, and may continue this metaphor by saying that the hydrogen atom 'at the top' can be split off, and a group of atoms can take its place –

$$\begin{array}{c} H \\ | \\ H-C-H \\ | \\ H-N-C-C \\ | \quad | \quad OH \\ H \quad H \end{array} \begin{array}{c} O \\ \end{array}$$

This is the formula for alanine, the next simplest of the amino acids; and all the others are built up in the same way – by the addition of groups of increasing complexity 'at the top'. It will be seen that the extremities 'at the bottom' are H and OH; and if one imagines a number of amino acids placed in line, the OH of the first will face the H of the second, and so on indefinitely. These three atoms constitute a molecule of water H_2O; and when the bond is formed that links the amino acids into long chains, this molecule of water drops out, and a new bond is established directly between N and C. This is dehydration synthesis. And its result, in this case, is a concatenation of various amino acids having a strong central axis, –N–C–C–, indefinitely repeating.

Such is the protein macromolecule. It may be a simple chain or a rope composed of several chains, and these may be folded, twisted, branched in numerous ways. All the twenty or so common amino acids may be present, they may be arranged in any order, and a single protein molecule may contain upwards of ten thousand of these units. The number of possible arrangements is therefore stupendous, and the fact that proteins are the main constituent of living bodies should not suggest a dull uniformity. To make a single specimen of every possible protein would require more matter than is contained in the whole Earth. For practical purposes, their variety is unlimited; and one may understand why this marvellous molecule provides an ideal basis for the diversity of life.

The only difference between the simple compounds that were present in the Earth's primeval atmosphere – methane, ammonia and water-vapour – and these complex chains is one of arrangement. They contain the same elements; and if the appropriate chemical transformations had taken place, the one could have given rise to the other. The question we have now to ask is whether, and if so how, this happened.

THE PATHWAYS TO LIFE

What is taking place – and why – in a chemical change? At the simplest, two atoms combine to form a molecule – as when two atoms of hydrogen unite to form a hydrogen molecule, H_2. But usually something more complicated is happening: some existing association between atoms or molecules is broken up, and its components enter into a new one. To achieve a new synthesis it is not enough that the reactants should be present, they must also be sufficiently excited. To initiate any change, energy is needed – the activation energy. This may be provided by light or heat, which disturbs the existing situation and leads to another.

In setting up their new configuration, the disturbed particles are always seeking a state of equilibrium – the most nearly perfect balance that the conditions of the moment permit. They do so by yielding to mutual attraction, and ending up as close as possible to the object that attracts them most. However restless they may seem to be, their motive is laziness – to reach the lowest energy level and to stay there. Although they arrange themselves, they are being continually disturbed;

and so one might say that the atoms dance reluctantly to a compelling, ceaseless music.

The forms of activation energy that were most readily available at the period of the Earth's history we are now discussing were electrical discharges in the atmosphere, sunlight far fiercer than it is today, and the local heating of rocks and water due to volcanism. Laboratory experiments simulating all of these, and using various mixtures of the primary atmospheric compounds, have been made; and all resulted in the synthesis of amino acids. This illuminating discovery has established that there were then several possible pathways leading towards life.

It may be that more than one of them was followed and that they converged on a single destination – the living cell; but the experiments made with hot volcanic rocks have proved especially interesting, because it was found that they yielded the amino acids that are commonly found in protein – but no others. This might explain why that special group became the basis of life. If thermal energy caused the synthesis, all the members of that group would have been available, at the same place and at the same time, for combining in the next stage of life-building.

The second stage in the process was the linking of the amino acids into simple protein chains; and the same experimental procedures have shown that any one of them could have led to this. But, once again, it was the experiments with hot volcanic rock that were the most revealing. Not only did thermal energy synthetize the special group that is now incorporated in living things, but also, when heating was sustained, bonds formed between them in sequences that are characteristic of a vital process. The so-called 'thermal pathways', in short, prefigure the biochemical order; and they suggest the emergence, in overlapping stages, of proteins and nucleic acids.

The nucleic acids are composed of the same elements as the proteins, with the addition of phosphorus. As the principles that account for the one will account for the other, it is not necessary to discuss their origin here; and their special significance will be considered later. What is chiefly of interest at this point is that the discovery of thermal pathways has shown that sequences that might appear to be unique to living organisms are, in reality, independent of life. Their order was determined by conditions in the pre-living world; it existed before the vital processes into which it has been incorporated; and in all probability it was simply taken over. It is now evident that there were several possible pathways to life. Its primary compounds were present in the Earth's atmosphere. Simple proteins and nucleic acids built out of them probably originated on the hot volcanic rocks and were then washed into the sea; but they might have been formed directly in the water, or they might have arisen in both localities. In any event, the sea was their meeting-place; and the first fully-living systems assembled in the water.

THE MISSING SYSTEM

Atoms, molecules, living cells – in the world-building process these are the familiar units or stages of construction. But there is something missing. Between the most advanced molecules and the most primitive cells, there is a space to be bridged. Viewed historically, this means the birth and development of a system. And if the theory advanced by Oparin and other biochemists is correct, it is a coacervate system. A coacervate – unlike atoms, molecules and cells – is not a familiar conception. But it may become so when the problem of life's origin is finally unravelled, for it would seem to be the missing link between the molecule and the cell.

We have reached a point in the story of the Earth when simple proteins and nucleic acids were present in its surface waters. The vast oceans of the present day did not then exist. They were gradually forming; but much of their water was still bound in the lithosphere, and the events we have now to describe took place in lakes, lagoons or shallow seas. These must have varied a great deal in temperature and in the chemical compounds they contained; and it may not have been in one locality only that the transition from the non-living to the living was made. All that can be said with certainty about the geography of this time is that it was completely different from that of today. So far as its surface features are concerned, the Earth might then have been a planet in another galaxy. We must imagine a landscape utterly strange – water and bare volcanic rock. Everything that now concerns us took place in the water.

Some large molecules, including the types we have been discussing, tend to come together when in solution in such a way that they form into layers – one of which is rich in content, while the other is merely a supporting liquid. This is coacervation, and the rich layer is a simple coacervate. The process does not stop at this point; but the grouping becomes more elaborate, and there develop in order complex and then multiple coacervate systems. Protoplasm, the substance of a living cell, is a complex, multiple coacervate; and according to Oparin's theory, it was by the process of coacervation that the first cells were formed.

This line of enquiry has been followed up in the laboratory; but it must be remembered that nature has one great advantage over science – her 'experiments' are pursued throughout hundreds of millions of years. That is the time-scale on which we have to think; and so we should not expect to see new living cells arise by coacervation in a test-tube. The laboratory in which this did once happen was of planetary dimensions, the number of experiments performed there was all but infinite, and the time devoted to them was something in the order of a thousand million years.

The formation of a coacervate system depends in the first place on the right concentration of its components, which does not need to be high, and the coming together of molecules bearing opposite electric charges. Once they are in association, weaker forces come to be important; and then distinct globules begin to form. It is, throughout, a process of self-synthesis: if the components parts of a mechanical system are piled in a heap, they remain inert; but when those of a chemical system are brought together, they begin to weave a pattern.

Certain droplets in a coacervate tend to concentrate nucleic acids. The surrounding world of these droplets is their containing globule, which may consist largely of simple proteins. This segregation suggests the architectural features of a living cell – a nucleus which is composed mainly of nucleic acids, surrounded by cytoplasm which is mainly protein. It is not, of course, necessary that the inner systems of a coacervate should enclose one another: they may be adjacent, or they may lie apart and yet be included in the main globule. This is the arrangement of the organelles of a cell, and offers a first hint of the varied morphology of life.

These inner parts must harmonize or the main system would be disrupted – indeed, it would never have come into existence at all. Element by element, reaction by reaction, a complex entity is thus gradually creating itself. Reciprocity and harmony are the determinants of its existence; it is only by compliance with these that it can come to be; and if it cannot maintain them, it will disintegrate. So arise the beauty and stability of living forms.

Even at this level, the notion of self-maintenance is not enough. If these activities had not also led to self-improvement, there would have been no life at all. Something, however, must always be maintained – namely the harmony between constituent parts; and as only certain elements conduce to this, while certain others would interfere with or disturb it, self-improvement entails a delicate process of mutual selection. One might even be tempted to say that it is on mutual selection that evolution hangs.

In a complex coacervate, as in a cell with its organelles, one consequence of the need for selectivity is the formation of a film or membrane, which delimits both the system as a whole and each internal part. This boundary both separates and unites: its characteristic is to be selective. It allows some substances to pass and repels others: it is a channel and a barrier. 'Thus there were formed entire multimolecular systems of coacervate drops, each of which already had a certain individuality in contrast to all the rest of the external world.'*

Oparin so states the kernel of his theory.

Its development in detail is too technical to be followed here; but what is gradually forming at this stage – the stage between the molecule and the cell – is a system. It is not just a pattern, it is something dynamic, it is something that works; and what makes a chemical system work is the presence of reaction chains.

We can now add something to our first definition of the life-process, and say that it is 'a network of chemical reactions co-ordinated in time'. Considered individually, each of these reactions is quite commonplace, and none is 'vital' in itself. It

*I. A. Oparin, *The Origin of Life on Earth*, 3rd edn., Oliver & Boyd 1957, p. 320.

is their summation, over a vast period of time, that constitutes such a marvellous phenomenon. The special character of a reaction chain, or chemical pathway, is that the energy released by one reaction is not dissipated, but harnessed so as to bring about the next. This is the nature of its continuity. And what we must picture is a flowing pattern of energy, accompanied by a transformation of substances at every step. This is the process of life.

One might compare the slow advance from a coacervate globule to the living cell with the change from a pioneer's hut to a thriving city. At the beginning, only a few tracks radiate from the hut: in the end, there is an elaborate network of communications. The pioneer himself did not make this plan, and the tracks sufficed for him. Their subsequent development, however, is altogether reasonable; and the city and the cell are equally the outcome of the logic of events in time.

THE PERPETUATION OF THE IMPROBABLE

It is not necessary that one molecule should 'give birth' to another in order to procure an abundance of water; because hydrogen and oxygen are common elements, and there is a strong probability that they will frequently meet and combine. Fortuity alone ensures that the atoms and a vast number of their compounds shall exist in plenty. But a race of hippopotami could hardly be continued by the chance encounter of constituent parts. A combination of great rarity, the probability of the formation of which is remote, might come into being once or a few times; but it cannot become plentiful unless it is able to duplicate itself. If it can do so, then even the most unlikely combination may grow to be common. And this is what life ensures – the perpetuation of the improbable.

To bring this about, the first thing that is necessary is a molecule that is able to copy itself. The nucleic acids have this ability, and that is why they are of such special importance. Every feature of a living body is the outcome of a long train of chemical events; and the starting-point of these events is a molecule situated in the nucleus of the cell – in other words, a gene. The function of the gene is first to duplicate itself, and then to initiate this creative sequence; and its active components, by which this is done, are nucleic acids. These are built of simpler units, the nucleotides, linked into chains; and centuries of speculation on the mysteries of reproduction and heredity were ended when the chemical secret of the nucleotides was discovered.

Each nucleotide consists of a phosphate, a sugar, and a base. The phosphates are all identical, there are two possible varieties of sugar, and four varieties of base. This seems a narrow choice. And on first thoughts it may appear incredible that the whole diversity of living form can be determined, at the outset, merely by juggling with such a paucity of parts. One can hardly reflect on this molecule, which makes life possible, without wonder; and yet its principle is not difficult to understand. It is made up of two strands twisted about each other to form a double spiral or helix. There are crosswise links holding the strands together, and so the spiral would resemble a ladder if it were unwound –

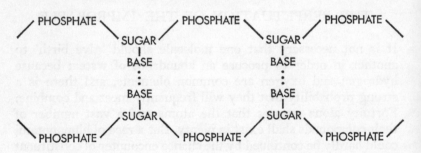

The 'ladder' must be pictured as prolonged indefinitely in both directions. The bonds that are shown by dashes are formed in the same way as those that link the amino acids – by the loss of a molecule of water, dehydration synthesis – and the resulting bond is strong. But the links between the bases, indicated by dots, are much weaker. They are only hydrogen bonds, formed by the tendency of a hydrogen atom to share its single electron between two neighbours – one in each base. Considered as a ladder, therefore, the nucleic acid molecule would be unsafe; the rungs would be liable to give way; but this weakness is its most precious advantage. The difference in strength between the two types of bonding permits the molecule, under certain circumstances, to split in half lengthwise;

and this is the first step towards complete duplication. The transmission of heredity would be impossible without this arrangement – one set of bonds that is easily broken and another that holds firm.

The second step is for each of the separated strands to attract to itself free nucleotides – there is a store of these in the nucleus – and so to replace its lost complement exactly. A new set of hydrogen bonds then forms between the bases. There are four kinds of base – cytosine, guanine, adenine and thymine – and the order in which they are arranged in each strand constitutes the genetic code. If the messages of heredity are to be transmitted correctly, this order must be preserved; and its preservation depends on the fact that each base has only one possible complement. No other will fit, and so the order in one strand completely determines the complementary order when the other is assembled. Cytosine must always face guanine, and adenine must always face thymine. It is on the shape of these four bases that genetic inheritance depends –

When these molecules approach one another and make contact, hydrogen bridges form along the lines of dots. The arrows indicate the stronger bonds by which the bases are attached to the sides of the 'ladder'. The sugars may be of two kinds; but as only one ever appears in the same strand, nucleic acids are distinguished accordingly – into RNA (ribonucleic acid), and DNA (deoxyribonucleic acid). DNA has one atom of oxygen less; and although this may seem a small matter, it has an important consequence. DNA is confined to the nucleus, whereas RNA is able to travel to other parts of the cell and there to set up chains of chemical activity.

One may be surprised at the fewness of the 'code symbols' which preserve the patterns of inheritance. But the Morse code, using only two symbols, a dot and a dash, is able to transmit every word in the language; and it has been calculated that the possible arrangements of the four nucleotides, in molecules as large as DNA, would exceed the number of atoms in the solar system. The only limit, therefore, to the variety of life-forms that could be represented by the genetic code is the capacity of the Earth to contain them.

Stress has been laid on the exactitude of the self-copying process; but it is clear that something so intricate must yield discrepancies from time to time; and influences from the outer world – some forms of radiation for example – may also disturb it. In such ways the 'coded message' may be accidentally changed. This alteration will be perpetuated when the molecule reduplicates, and may result in some wholly novel feature in the finished organism. This is a mutation – one of the fundamental causes of evolutionary change.

The vast majority of mutations are harmful. When they occur in the higher forms of life, many result in the death of the embryo, or, if the organism should achieve independent existence, in its death in infancy, or, if maturity is reached, in its being killed and devoured by those that are better equipped. There are millions of failures, with an immensity of attendant suffering, for every mutational success. But evolution requires that there shall be major stabilities and minor variations; that offspring shall be much the same as their parents, but not quite the same; and that both the similarity and the difference shall be inheritable. The idea that evolution is the plan of some extraneous intelligence can hardly survive these considerations: the intelligence is intrinsic – gradually realized and increasingly displayed.

The frontier between the non-living and the living is not marked by any chasm in nature, and the events we have described fill a vast intermediate territory which took millions of years to traverse; but with the emergence of a molecule able to copy itself and to initiate events that duplicate a whole system, a new world has been entered and a new era begun. Once established, life's methods are conservative. The genes in the cell nucleus are strung together like beads on a varying number of threads – the chromosomes; and all of them are built on the same structural principles. The first ever 'seen' were those in a pollen grain. When Buchholz photographed the chromosomes of corn pollen under an electron microscope, in 1945, dark structures showed in them which proved to be genes. And so, from the wind-blown pollen to the reproductive cells of man, similar messengers carry the patterns of life and bear witness to its unity.

THE CELL COMMUNITY

The dawn of life cannot be dated exactly. The earliest geological evidence of it comes from Rhodesia, recorded in some of the world's most ancient rocks. The age of these rocks, determined by the breakdown of their radioactive elements, is about two thousand seven hundred million years. They contain secretions of lime, which were made by living organisms. The ability to secrete lime, as a protective covering, must have taken some time to acquire; and so it is a fair assumption that there were living cells in existence by 3,000,000,000 B.P.

The next geological evidence comes from Canada. These rocks are about a thousand million years younger than the Rhodesian series. The first real fossils that have yet been found are contained in them – they are the fossils of minute aquatic plants. There was, in fact, a flora. The coming of a flora is important for several reasons; but the most obvious is that plants are not one-celled, but many-celled organisms. A new structural theme had emerged.

Even stars and dinosaurs cannot continue to grow bigger indefinitely, and at every stage of evolution there is a problem of maximum size. If an atomic nucleus contains more than about ninety protons, it becomes unstable and the atom transmutes into a lighter element; if a molecule becomes larger than the common proteins and nucleic acids, it breaks up spontaneously; and when a cell grows beyond a certain size, which is usually still microscopic, the nucleus can no longer exert effective control over the cytoplasm, and the cell divides into two. To every phase there is a limit. But this does not bring evolution to a halt; because when each unit has been perfected, it becomes a building-block in a larger one. It does not thereby lose its own character and identity; but the larger structure, created by association, displays new properties which could not otherwise have existed. These properties are, so to speak, themes in the world-music; and when countless variations have been played on each of them individually, it is incorporated into a more ambitious composition.

It might, therefore, have been predicted that once life had established itself in the form of separate, diversifying cells, there would be a new synthesis – a multicellular organism. This was at first – and essentially has always remained – a community, in which the cells kept together when they multiplied instead of drifting apart. Their ability to diversify was thereafter exploited in a more disciplined way. By remaining in contact, the cells created an environment for one another; and each had to adapt to this environment or it could not live. The new discipline required compatibility, and it selected variations that were for mutual good. This involved some loss of freedom, but there were stupendous compensations.

When a cell divides, the genes are duplicated exactly. And as a multicellular organism begins as a single cell and grows by repeated divisions, it follows that all the cells in it, however diverse they may be, contain exactly the same genetic pattern. This may appear somewhat mysterious; but it is explained by the fact that while there is practically no limit to what the code of the nucleotides can represent, there is a very narrow limit to what the body of a single cell can realize. One nucleus, therefore, may contain immeasurably more possibilities than one cytoplasm can express; and to find complete expression, it may need the cytoplasm of very many cells. In each one of these only a small fraction of the genetic message will be interpreted in living form, but all of it will be encoded. This makes it possible, under suitable conditions, for one cell to give rise to an entire organism.

Reproduction by simple cell division is efficient; but from the standpoint of evolution, it has a drawback. If it is performed perfectly, the offspring will be all alike; and natural selection can work only if it is offered a choice. It is true that the process allows for some choice; because it will not always proceed perfectly, and there will be genetic mutations from time to time. But mutation is a dangerous thing; and although some of the great advances of evolution have been due to it, it is far more likely to do harm than good. A safer way to diversity was desirable; and after millions of years of natural 'experiment', it was found. It was sexual reproduction. This makes the fusion of two cells from different parents the starting-point; and so the new individual will not be identical with either, but inherit some of the characters of each.

The cells that fuse in sexual reproduction differ from all other cells in having only half the normal complement of genes. They are said to be haploid, and the others diploid. When they unite, the full number is restored. The formation of haploid cells requires a special kind of preliminary division – reduction division – and it took a long time to work out this process. The events that led up to it are not fully understood; but it may have been survival under conditions of adversity, not reproduction, that was the original aim. Some one-celled organisms are able to enclose themselves in a protective covering when circumstances are unfavourable. Then they wait, their vital activities suspended, until a propitious change permits them to discard their armour and return to life. Sometimes two cells fuse before the resistant coat is formed; and although in such cases there is no sexual difference between them, and the purpose is merely survival, sex-union might have evolved from this; and multicellular organisms might have adapted the device by producing complementary cells. In any case, however it arose, sex was a great success; because it provided a safe and gentle method of ensuring diversity.

All animals and nearly all plants employ this means of reproduction; but the plants still bear witness to the fact that sex is not an absolute necessity. A single unfertilized cell can give rise to a new individual: such a cell is a spore. The plants make use of both methods, and that is why their reproduction is so complicated. Only the very simplest forms of life have no recourse to sex, and its 'invention' must be accounted one of nature's triumphs.

With these factors at work – mutation and sex – evolution was provided with a wide field of choice. They ensure that new individuals shall be near-copies but not replicas of their progenitors. Most will be closely similar to the parental type, which may therefore persist through vast periods with little alteration; some will be inferior, or less suited to their surroundings, and they will perish quickly; a few will show improvements, enabling them to respond better to the demanding world, and these will live longer and be more prolific. There are three happenings, therefore, that we should expect – the persistence of an ancestral pattern, the disappearance of most collateral branches, and the progressive transformation of others. In studying the course of evolution, the stress falls so strongly on the lives that are undergoing progressive transformation that there is a tendency to forget something that should be kept in mind – apart from our slight knowledge of extinct forms, we know nothing of the experiments that failed. We are following the fortunes of the successful few.

PLANTS AND ANIMALS

The coming of a flora – which was, of course, entirely aquatic, there was no land-life whatever at this time – is important for another reason. The animal kingdom is dependent on the plants not only for food but also for breath. A plant makes its own food out of simple non-living compounds, but this is something that an animal cannot do. The plant takes in carbon dioxide and water, breaks them up, re-arranges their parts, and recombines them as a sugar. The sugar, however, needs only the hydrogen from the water – the oxygen is set free. The animals require the sugars to eat and the free oxygen to breathe; and until the plants had furnished the world with these necessities, no animals could exist.

Some two thousand million years ago, or even earlier than that, certain organisms that might be called proto-plants encountered and began to incorporate porphryns. A porphryn is a ring-shaped molecule built round a central atom, which is sometimes iron, but in the variety that the plants use is magnesium. The substance that makes plants green, chlorophyll, is a porphryn with a magnesium atom in the centre. Various groups may be attached to the outside of the ring, but the inner part has this structure –

The importance of this ring of atoms, chlorophyll, is that it is able to trap the energy of sunlight and to use this to release chemical energy. The process is still not completely understood; but magnesium must be essential to it, and what is thought to happen is that an electron in this atom absorbs a photon of light, becomes excited, and initiates a series of electron transfers which provide energy for the making of a sugar and the liberation of oxygen. To the animals this means food and breath. In every leaf and seaweed these activities are now taking place; but until an atom of magnesium began dancing to the Sun in the centre of the porphryn ring, the animal kingdom could not come into existence.

Oxygen is a common element, but most of the Earth's supply was bound in compounds until the plants released it. The animals need it in a free state. To maintain the flowing patterns of life, the right amount of energy must be available at the appropriate place and time; and this precision is achieved by the making and breaking of chemical bonds. When atoms are grouped to form a molecule, some energy is required to hold them in that particular configuration. This is their bonding energy; and whenever the configuration is altered – as it always is when a chemical reaction takes place – the amount needed to maintain it will also change. Every chemical reaction, therefore, will either release energy or absorb it; and part of the trick of life is to take in substances such as sugars that have a great deal stored in their bonds, and by subjecting them to chemical changes, to release this when and where it is required. Free oxygen is not indispensible to such a process, but it adds immensely to its efficiency.

61

Before free oxygen was available for respiration, life had recourse to other methods of energy-release. One of these was fermentation, and to compare the results of fermentation with those of respiration is to see at once how great was the gain. Both begin with sugar, and break it down; but the end products of fermentation are carbon dioxide and alcohol, those of respiration are carbon dioxide and water, and the latter process releases over twenty-four times the amount of energy. It is the use of free oxygen that makes the difference. Fermentation is, however, a possible method of energy-release; and according to Oparin's theory it was the earlier one on which respiration was subsequently imposed. Some writers have remarked that this gain also entailed a certain loss, and they have speculated with regret on the permanent euphoria that might have been enjoyed by the higher forms of life if they had continued to evolve with an energy metabolism of which the end-product is alcohol instead of water. It was due to the plants that life sobered down at such an early stage.

Plants and animals have the same origin, and all that has been said of living cells up to this point applies to both. It was, in fact, by a study of sweet-peas that Mendel first penetrated the secrets of human heredity. They have followed different paths of evolution, however, for more than a thousand million years; and it was their contrasting methods of obtaining energy and food that caused them to diverge. When some cells discovered how to trap the energy of light and to use it to make their own food out of simple substances that were easily obtainable, the more elaborate organisms that descended from them had only to spread themselves in the sunlight – either to float, or to become rooted in some favourable spot. But cells that could not make their own food had to go and find it. It was seldom abundant, and often rapidly consumed. The larger organisms that developed from them had to learn to move about, to discriminate between food and non-food, and between localities where it was profitable or unprofitable to search.

So arose the great divide which natural selection has steadily accentuated. Members of the vegetable kingdom exhibit innumerable answers to one main problem – how to settle down peacefully in the sun. Members of the animal kingdom show various solutions to two problems – how to move quickly and how to acquire a discriminating sense.

CHAPTER THREE

Consciousness

PSYCHE

The word 'consciousness' will be used here in its fundamental
sense – namely, as the prerequisite of any kind of awareness,
sensation or perception whatsoever. To be without consciousness, in this usage, is to be in oblivion.

Despite many gaps in knowledge, there is fairly wide
agreement on the course of evolution that has so far been
described; but consciousness is a controversial subject which
cannot be presented in the same way. It still belongs more to
philosophy than to science, and philosophers have been wrangl-
ing over it for centuries without becoming agreed. A meaningful study of evolution, however, cannot evade this question;
and if there is not a certain answer, there must be at least a
reasonable surmise as to how and when consciousness, in this
fundamental sense, arose. Is it an attribute of all living things?

The difficulty in making a reply comes from the fact that
consciousness is a private matter. I know that I am conscious,
but I cannot directly observe consciousness in anyone else.
I assume it, but that is an inference based on analogy: 'I am
conscious; all human beings are like me; therefore, all human
beings are conscious.' The conclusion is not logically necessary,
only probable; and the argument cannot be put in a form that
would make the conclusion necessary. It all hangs on the word
'like', and on how far the likeness extends. Few people would
doubt that the conclusion in this case is sound, but let us
suppose that the second premise is made more sweeping: 'All
atoms are like me.' This is true to the extent that the atoms
and I are both composed of protons, electrons and whatever
other sub-atomic particles there may be. But we should be
reluctant to conclude that all atoms are therefore conscious,
although it cannot be proved that they are not.

If we descend the ladder of evolution from ourselves to the
atoms asking at each rung, 'Does *like* still include consciousness?'
then, unless we can attach consciousness to some demonstrable
physical quantity which at a certain point disappears – and this
seems to be impossible – every answer must be a guess. We
may suppose that at some point in evolution a minute quantum
of consciousness first arises, but there is nothing to guide us

in determining that point except probability. Does it probably coincide with the emergence of life?

'From the unicellular organism to man, no new principle is needed,'* is one of the more provocative assertions of Behaviourism. Whether it is true or not depends on what is meant by a principle; but there is no doubt that a single free-living cell carries out, in its own simple way, the same vital activities as a higher animal. It is capable of ingestion and excretion, respiration and reproduction, the reception and conduction of stimuli, and of behaviour that suggests sentience or elementary consciousness.

All these are observable except consciousness; and as that is never observable, it would be arbitrary to suppose that it alone is lacking when all these measurable activities are there. 'We cannot avoid the conclusion', according to Sir Julian Huxley, 'that minute mind-like activities accompany all the processes of living matter.'† No doubt we could avoid this conclusion, but it is a reasonable hypothesis. What, however, is meant by a mind-like activity?

Stimulus and response are universal in principle. Every star, every planet, every atom responds to changes in its surroundings and may also initiate changes in itself. There are no absolute frontiers in nature; but there are functional frontiers, within which each system behaves as a unit. And so there come to be systems within systems, interacting with or responding to one another; and when we arrive at living organisms, we find ourselves speaking of a psychical system within a physical system – of a mind within a body. Mind and body suggest a chasm; but the words are our inventions, and the chasm, perhaps, is our illusion.

An interaction between an organism and its environment is physical in its beginning and its ending – the stimulus is physical and so is the observable response; but in the interval between them, something is happening which, in higher organisms at least, it is customary to call a mental operation. In psychological terms, it involves an act of perception, an attribution of meaning, and a decision between possible responses.

*J. B. Watson, *Behaviour: An Introduction to Comparative Psychology*, Holt, New York, 1914, p. 318.
†'Science and God', *Observer*, 17 July, 1960.

Is this intervening activity essentially different from what comes before and after? If we attempt to follow the mediating process between external stimulus and external response – cell to cell, molecule to molecule, atom to atom – we reach a point when these physical terms and concepts fail to express what we need to say. The 'mind-like activities' have taken over, and they themselves are organized. A psyche has emerged. Although the psyche is elusive, it is not amorphous: it is something, as psychoanalysis has shown, that also has a structure. The difference between this structure and the physical structure, between subject and object, is not, however, an essential difference. Somewhere in the passage between stimulus and response, we travel through a region that we are obliged to term metaphysical; but we still have not crossed, and never could cross, an absolute frontier.

If this seems strange, it is because we have been tempted to think that we know what matter and energy really are. But we do not know. They are expressions of something which, in certain of its phases, can be described in the language of physics and chemistry, but which none the less remains elusive in its real nature. In itself, this essence does not alter when the physical becomes the psychical; but it is then realizing potentialities that such terms as mass, force and inertia cannot describe. If we are to speak of them, we need the language of psychology – sensation, emotion, volition – or psychoanalytical terms. It is evident that all our legitimate questions cannot be expressed in the language of the physical sciences; and even in nuclear physics, the old materialism has crumbled.

The psyche, which is a metaphysical system, arises naturally out of the mediating process between stimulus and response. It is brought into being, in the first place, to ensure that the response shall be appropriate. To achieve this, the nature of both the stimulating object and the responding subject must be taken into account; and the subject is infinitesimally changed by its experience, because this has been recorded. In establishing an adequate relationship between itself and its environment, a living organism is thus gradually acquiring an understanding of both; and since organisms that fail to do this soon perish, it is evident that there is a steady evolutionary pressure towards the acquisition of knowledge, of which self-knowledge is one aspect. This leads to a sense of distinction between the self – all that lies inside the functional frontier that bounds the system as a unit – and the not-self beyond. And in the whole drama of evolution there can hardly be a more significant event than this – the emergence of a feeling subject to whom the world is object.

From the assumption that 'minute mind-like activities accompany all the processes of living matter' it follows that even the most elementary lives have this psychical potentiality; but it will not evolve any further unless there are reasons why it should. In the animal kingdom, where the need is to move quickly and to develop a discriminating sense, there are compelling reasons; but in the plant kingdom, settling peacefully in the sunlight, there are scarcely any. The animals require nerves, while the plants do not; and the psyche, in the next phase of its evolution, is virtually the creation of a nervous system.

THE NERVE-CELL

The first distinct nerve-cells, and the beginnings of nervous organization, are found in the Coelenterates. There are many genera, both extinct and surviving, of this primitive phylum; it would be almost true to say that it represents the fundamental animal; and it is probably ancestral to all the higher groups. A still-living member is the jelly-fish; and it therefore seems appropriate that in the Grand Canyon, where a magnificent rock sequence is displayed, the only fossil yet discovered in the Pre-Palaeozoic strata is that of a jelly-fish. It must be considerably more than six hundred million years old; and as the jelly-fish is a well-developed member of its phylum, nervous systems have been evolving for perhaps a thousand million years. There had been life, of course, for a very long time before that; but it had managed without nerves. With the advent of nerves, the tempo of evolution quickens.

The cells that compose a nervous system do not differ from others except in specialization. They have become adapted to serve the cell-community by performing a particular task. There are now many varieties of nerve-cell; but the jelly-fish has only two kinds, and both are so primitive that they have been almost completely superseded in more advanced animals. At the surface, it has neuro-sensory cells, which project a sensitive 'hair' responsive to external stimuli, and an opposite thread-like process conducting inwards. In higher organisms, stimuli are received by uniquely specialized cells – the primary receptors – which respond to one kind of stimulus only. The old neuro-sensory cells then retreat, as it were, and receive their stimulation at second-hand. They have become true nerve-cells or neurones. Their sensitive 'hair' grows branches – the dendrites – each of which is in touch with a group of primary receptors; and the more numerous and selective these receptors are, the more discriminating is perception. The jelly-fish has hardly begun to discriminate, and it can have only a vague inner world – merely a sense of light and balance.

Nerve-cells of the second type spread the impulse that the neuro-sensory cells impart to them. They lie deeper, and form a nerve-net and nerve-rings. As this network conducts in all directions, it provides no true nervous pathways, but only a plexus through which impulses are diffused. Even in ourselves these primitive types are still represented: there are neuro-sensory cells in the retina of the eye, and there are some like those of the ancient nerve-net in our visceral regions. Otherwise, we rely on thousands of millions of neurones, which permit an incomparable flexibility, delicacy and exactitude.

Although there are many kinds of neurone, they have a common pattern which could be compared with an outspread hand. The fingers would represent the dendrites, fine outgrowths which receive the excitation from primary receptors or from another nerve-cell; the palm of the hand would represent the cell-body, where its individual life is carried on; and the arm would be the axon, a long fibre which carries the impulse to another nerve-cell, or sometimes to a muscle or a gland. The impulse is electrical in the nerve-fibres and could travel in either direction; but it passes from the axon of one cell to the dendrites of another by the diffusion of a chemical substance, and this ensures a one-way flow. A system of marvellous subtlety and precision has been built up in the higher animals on these principles; but this is the last refinement of evolution, and to float with eyes closed and ears stopped on a sunlit sea is perhaps to recapture something of the first nervous experience of life.

MUTUAL CREATION

The whole organism is brought into being as a system of responses, and in that sense it is a product of environmental creation. Its perception arises in the first place to guide its responses. If it did not respond appropriately, it could not live; and the fact that it does live is evidence that its perceptions are not illusions. At the same time, in the act of responding, it becomes part of the creative environment of others, a cause of their responses, so that the whole living complex is one of mutual creativity.

Discrimination is of cardinal importance to this process; and discrimination depends on the ability of certain cells – the primary receptors – to become highly specialized. Each different mode of energy – light, heat, vibration – has a different cause in the outer world, and so carries a different kind of information. Each must be distinguished separately, and then all must be combined into a unified pattern of meaning. This is the guide to a pattern of action. A perception is not a mere reflection as in a looking-glass: the reflection is of no importance to the looking-glass, but to an organism, the perception may be a matter of life and death.

When a receptor cell is stimulated by the special mode of energy to which it has learnt to respond, it awakens a nerve-cell, and the disturbance then takes the form of a nerve-impulse. This inner effect is very different from the external cause. It is not a copy of outside events, but represents them symbolically. It is a coded message, and the perception is its interpretation.

To understand how this symbol becomes an object of consciousness, insofar as this can be understood, one must consider the nervous activity that gives rise to it. Nerve-cells have become adapted to fulfil three main functions. There are sensory cells in contact with the receptors; there are motor cells which touch and direct the muscles and glands; and between these, as intermediaries, there are co-ordinating cells, which evaluate the information flowing in from many receptors and determine the response. This work of co-ordinating and evaluation requires the formation of nerve-centres. These grow in number and complexity as organisms and their needs become more elaborate; and there gradually develops a hierarchy of centres, in the highest of which occurs the act of perception.

This experience and attribution of meaning can be discussed only in psychological terms. The psychical has emerged from the physical – a mind from a body; and a living organism cannot, therefore, be understood in the same way as a molecule or a combustion engine. If one admits only physical criteria, one simply fails to understand it. In the words of Professor Thorpe, 'subjective concepts derived from introspection are among the essential tools for the study of life.'*

A mindless zoology, the notion of 'animal machines', makes organic evolution incomprehensible; because the greatest achievement of the animal kingdom is the creation of conscious subjects to whom the rest of the world is an object of experience. This emergence of the psyche introduces a new theme – the communication of self with self, of mind with mind, and their mutual exploration. Two butterflies hovering and turning about each other, two birds circling, evading, mating, two puppies playing together, a pair of lovers hand-in-hand – these are all stages in the endeavour of minds to communicate with one another.

Because mind eludes our physical categories, there are some philosophers who would like to dismiss the concept altogether as a 'category mistake'. But the world is not wholly comprised in physical categories, and the concept of minds is as necessary as that of atoms. If language is to symbolize experience, there must also be a word for 'self' – for a subject to whom the world is object and who seeks to communicate with other subjects. The status of being a 'self' is seemingly a consequence of the possession of a nervous system; and long before the butterflies, nervous systems were elaborate.

THE SEAT OF CONSCIOUSNESS

It is natural to speak, at least metaphorically, of a 'seat' of consciousness. But if there is a spark of consciousness in every cell, why, in higher organisms, is it so narrowly restricted to certain regions of the nervous system? That it is so restricted is a matter of experience; how this is brought about has not

*W. H. Thorpe, *Learning and Instinct in Animals*, Methuen 1956, p. 7.

yet been adequately explained; but why it is desirable, in fact necessary, presents a simpler problem. An analogy will help to make this clear.

If one looks at the open back of a watch, one sees a complicated mechanism: if one looks at the front, one sees the time. Whatever seeing the time may mean, it is something very different from looking at the works. Gazing at the works, one might think: 'This little wheel turns that . . . that spring moves this . . . humm, does it?' One may make sense of it, or one may not; but it will not be the same kind of sense as is to be had from a quick glance at the front: 'It's twelve o'clock!' From looking at the machinery, one would never know that it was twelve o'clock; and yet the machinery exists in order that the time shall be known.

The unconscious depths of the psyche are likewise extremely complex; but they also exist, at least in the first place, in order that a simple unified perception shall arise, permitting instant and appropriate action. On the speed of this action may hang life and death. It might have been possible for the field of consciousness to have been more extensive – it might, perhaps, have included all the 'works'; but if it had done so, it would have been a dangerous liability. It would have confused the issue, and the issue was not infrequently survival. It is therefore just as important that consciousness should be restricted in some ways as that it should be extended in others. And although we do not understand how it was brought about, we can appreciate that it was necessary that the psyche should evolve as a mainly unconscious function, vastly complex in its depths, but with a small 'surface' of consciousness displaying the immediately relevant state of affairs.

This restriction implies a 'seat' of consciousness – that is, a special area where the phenomenon occurs. It has not always been in the same place. As higher nervous centres became available in the course of evolution, it would seem that the seat of consciousness was progressively transferred from the 'old brain' to the 'new'; and despite all that remains mysterious about this process, it is clear that there were sound biological reasons why it should occur – reasons of life and death.

Physically one must speak of a region, but psychologically of an act – the act of attention. At every instant there are countless nervous stimuli, and countless memories, that could enter the field of consciousness if they were attended to, but which in fact do not. They are consigned to oblivion by one of the most primitive of all psychological processes – habituation. Thorpe has illustrated habituation by the behaviour of a snail crawling over a pane of glass. If the glass is tapped, the snail stops, draws back into its shell, waits a little, and then moves on again. If the taps are repeated, it will do this several times; but eventually it will continue its promenade without concern and take no more notice of the taps. This is habituation.

In the snail's behaviour, which is necessary to efficient living, there is implicit logic; and even the simplest animal must act logically or it could not survive. In effect, judgments and deductions are made, conclusions are drawn, and causality is exploited. Logic is a living process before it is discovered, and all that the logician can do better than the snail is to account for his behaviour syllogistically: 'Those taps are a sign of possible danger; all signs of possible danger are to be acted on by retreat; therefore, those taps are to be acted on by retreat.' The logician thereupon withdraws into his shell, but the rational discourse continues: 'Those taps are followed by nothing; everything that is followed by nothing is to be ignored; therefore, those taps are to be ignored.' The logician comes out; the taps go on; but he is now unconscious of them, and is attending to something more important. The experience has been recorded, and in the future it will be needless to spend any time on similar taps. The snail does all this: the logician explains it. But in fact he is only a late-comer, who takes notice of a living process, splits it into little bits, and calls them S and P.

It was a condition of survival that consciousness should be restricted, and that evolving minds should be shaped from the beginning in a rational form. An organism is a piece of living logic, and its psychical life is a product of its physical life. The psyche and the nervous system must therefore evolve concurrently, and this reciprocity is characteristic of animal evolution. The body is a loom on which a mind is being woven.

When my dog pushes open the door, greets me, and settles down by the fire, I may wonder, What opened the door? A nose? A paw? No; it was a mind, directing the nose and the paw. That mind is not radically different from my own; both rest on a brain of similar design, and both permit us, among many other things, to find pleasure in each other's company and in sitting together in front of the fire. The neural structure that underlies my mind is more elaborate, but quite comparable with his; and in both of us the seat of consciousness has been transferred from the old brain to the new. My chief advantage is that the sensory areas in my brain are surrounded by a much larger number of co-ordinating cells, and this permits me to extract more meaning from my perceptions. His capacity for sensations and images is probably equal to mine, but he is not so good at concepts. In both of us, however, the brain has reached a stage of inconceivable complexity; and to understand ourselves and our friendship, we must look back to its beginning and trace the evolution of this structure that we share.

CHAPTER FOUR

The Palaeozoic World

BIOSPHERE AND PSYCHOSPHERE

The biosphere, the part of the Earth that lives, evolved naturally from the non-living Earth; and within it, to guide the responses of living organisms, a psyche arose. This event seems more mysterious, but it is no less natural. Since the psyche eludes the language that describes physical bodies, and cannot be accounted for in terms of matter and its behaviour, there arises the question of whether it may also elude physical confinement. If there should be evidence that it does, this would involve no contradiction; and evidence alone can provide the answer.

Sir Alister Hardy has suggested that telepathy may have been a factor in evolution,* and others have proposed it as an explanation of some forms of insect behaviour. If they are correct, it would of course follow that psychical activities are not confined within the bodies where they first arose; and to recognize from the beginning that this is a possibility has the advantage of leaving room, as it were, for evidence that may come later. In any case, whether it is confined within bodies or not, psychical life is organized concurrently with physical life; and the evolution of a biosphere entails the evolution of a psychosphere.

We cannot observe the evolution of the psyche; but we may – indeed, we must – assume it as we trace that of the bodies that were its loom. There is an unbroken record of bodies since the opening of the Palaeozoic Era about 600,000,000 B.P. That is not, of course, to imply that the fossil record contains and has yielded to search a sample of every form of life; but it is sufficiently detailed to display the main lines of evolution, to make it possible to correlate the rocks in different parts of the world, and to place them, according to the fossils they have preserved, in a relative temporal sequence.

Originally, the Earth had no surface water; this was gradually emitted from the lithosphere. But when the Palaeozoic Era began, and for some while before that, the oceans had attained their present volume. They were not, however, in their present places. Three-quarters of the Earth's surface is now

*Sir Alister Hardy, Lecture IX, 'Biology and Telepathy', *The Living Stream*, Collins, 1965.

covered by water; and if it were a perfect sphere, there would be a universal ocean several thousand feet deep. It is only the surface irregularities – deep ocean basins and high continental masses – that prevent this; and as the Earth's crust is never still, and no feature of it is really stable, the land is in constant danger from the sea.

A slight sinking of the continental platforms or a small uplift of the ocean floor is cataclysmic, and inundations have been frequent throughout geological time. Again and again, shallow seas have spread across America and Russia, left evidence of their presence in the rocks, and then withdrawn. Some geologists believe that there is a rhythm in these marine transgressions, and have written of the 'pulse-beat of the Earth'.

THE ARTHROPODS

The Early Palaeozoic was a time when shelf-seas were tending to expand; and as all animal life was then still restricted to the water, this expansion favoured it, and the age was one of increasing opportunity. Although this is the beginning of the fossil record, nearly all the main phyla of the animal kingdom – that is to say, its primary divisions or sub-kingdoms – were already distinct; but only very few traces of their evolution before this time have been preserved.

When the record first became continuous, about six hundred million years ago, the most advanced phylum was that of the Arthropods. At the present day, the Arthropods, which include the insects, are more numerous and varied than all the other phyla put together; and through the whole history of the Earth, they have been the pioneers of life. In the Early Palaeozoic they were represented by two species now extinct, the trilobites and the eurypterids, which were then the vanguard of evolution. Towards the middle of the era, members of the Arthropoda were the first animals to colonize the land, and for a long time they had the continents to themselves. They were the first to conquer the air, millions of years before the flying-lizards or the birds. They were the first to have elaborate social systems – such as those of the ants and the bees – to which our own moralists have sometimes pointed as exemplary. It is probable that they were the first to use symbols of communication, which we are only just beginning to understand, such as the dance-language of the bees; and it is even possible that they were the first to exploit telepathy. In all likelihood, furthermore, they will be the last multicellular animals to survive on Earth when, as the astronomers predict, it is finally shrivelled up by an expanding Sun. Alpha, and perhaps omega. The Arthropods must be looked on with respect.

Despite their remoteness in time, their subsequent extinction, and the forbidding names they have so lately acquired, the first-known animals have an enduring fascination. Compared with the inexhaustible variety of present-day life, species were then few, and opportunities were many. Countless living-spaces were still undefended, the conditions of survival can seldom have been less exacting, and so the animals underwent a great radial evolution and developed novel and curious forms. They put a girdle round the Earth, and the same types are found everywhere. Life was unhurried in their sunlit waters. The Palaeozoic Era lasted three hundred and seventy-five million years; and for about a third of that time the trilobites, the nautiloids and the eurypterids enjoyed their supremacy.

More than a thousand species of trilobite have so far been discovered, and it is on their sequential development that the dating of the Early Palaeozoic rocks mainly depends – they are the guide-fossil. But after this long period of astonishing fecundity, they began to dwindle, and by the end of the era they had disappeared. The history of the trilobites affords a first example of a pattern that will be found in many races – a rapid early radiation, an age of dominance, a long ineffectual struggle against rising competitors, and a final relegation to the record of the rocks. It is an oft-told story. And only those among us who have the luck to become fossils will be a green memory in six hundred million years.

THE ORIGIN OF THE CHORDATES

A phylum of which there is no record in the Early Palaeozoic rocks is that of the Chordates. The Chordates include all animals with a backbone – the vertebrates proper – and also their forerunners, who possessed a flexible rod-like structure,

79

the notocord, which evolved into a backbone. This is the phylum to which we belong. Did it exist when the fossil record began but left no trace, or did it arise later from one of the established groups? There is no certain answer, but there are two lines of speculation.

It has been said of the Coelenterates, the phylum to which the jelly-fish belong, that it represents the 'fundamental animal'. If the epithet is deserved, it must be ancestral to all the other phyla; but without fossil evidence this could not be proved. The Coelenterates have radial symmetry: like flowers and stars, they are more or less the same all round. For an animal that does little more than float, or that attaches itself to a firm base, as many Coelenterates do, and settles down to an almost plant-like existence, this shape is appropriate. But it is quite unsuited to an active animal. And as mobility offered great evolutionary advantage, bilateral symmetry was developed early. All the higher organisms have it – a front-end and a back-end, ultimately head and feet, and a variety of appendages in pairs. The transition from radial to bilateral symmetry took place before the fossiliferous ages, and the sequence of events is therefore conjectural. It is not difficult to conceive, however, that a bag-shaped animal might become elongated, and so move that the mouth-end went in front. Bilateral symmetry would be a rational adaptation to this mode of life. Perhaps many experiments were made, and certainly two were successful – successful in the sense that each of them gave rise to major groups that have continued to this day. One group includes all the bilaterally symmetrical animals that have no backbone, and the other, those that have. And the invertebrates came first.

To grapple with the problem of vertebrate origins, since there is no fossil evidence, we are obliged to turn to the still-living evidence of embryology, and of some curious intermediate forms. In embryological development, from a single fertilized cell to the adult organism, the course of evolution is in a sense recapitulated; and in this brief span of time each individual makes a rapid journey along a road that took hundreds of millions of years to build. This recapitulation is not, of course, made in every detail; it is an adumbration of past events, and requires skilled interpretation. But none the less, in a certain sense, each one of us has re-lived, as an individual, the whole unfolding process of life on Earth. And it is often by comparative embryology that the intricate relationships of the great family are most lucidly displayed.

On the problem of vertebrate origins, the evidence of embryology is surprising. On the face of it, the answer it suggests seems improbable. It relates the Chordates to the Echinoderms. The Chordates are all long-bodied, and have the two-sided symmetry of paired limbs and sense-organs. The Echinoderms have an entirely different pattern. Among their surviving forms are the starfishes, sea-urchins, and sea-lilies. They are all marine animals, and, as the names of some of them suggest, they are radially symmetrical, having star-shaped or flower-like forms. That they themselves should have arisen from the more primitive Coelenterates presents no great problem; but how is it conceivable that they should have given rise to the Chordates – that the rod-shaped should be descended from the star-shaped?

One answer that has been suggested is neotony. Some animals have different forms at different stages of their development – every butterfly was once a caterpillar, and every frog a tadpole – and it occasionally happens that an immature form develops some adult characteristics and becomes able to reproduce itself without completing its cycle of change. This is neotony, and it has occasionally given rise to a new population. The supposition is that the Chordates arose from the Echinoderms by neotony. But the Early Palaeozoic Echinoderms that we should think of as ancestral were not active animals like the starfishes or sea-urchins; they anchored themselves to a rock or a stone by a long, flexible stalk. Such were the crinoids. Although they were true animals, they looked like flowers; and even palaeontologists have written of 'prairies of crinoids' in the Palaeozoic seas. One of the most beautiful of fossils, which could almost be mistaken for a work of art, is the group of crinoids, like giant lilies, in the South Kensington Museum.

Before becoming rooted to their rocks, the stalked Echinoderms pass through an active stage. During their larval period, they have bilateral symmetry, and swim by rhythmic movements of their slender bodies. In this form, they look like, and probably are, the first sketch of a Chordate; and several lines of evidence have led to the theory that some of these became arrested in their development, reached sexual maturity in their larval shape, and were thus able to exploit the great advantages of remaining active and bilaterally symmetrical in adult life. So, it is thought, arose the Chordate pattern, leading to the vertebrate pattern, and finally to the human pattern.

It must, however, be admitted that the origin of the Chordates remains in the realm of theory; and there is an alternative hypothesis. It is possible that bilateral symmetry came by direct evolution from the Coelenterates, and that the radial symmetry of the Echinoderms is the specialization of a side-line. Romer has advanced this point of view:

> In the dawn of the world, there existed some type of small, bilaterally symmetrical animal of very simple structure possessing many of the features of the larval echinoderm . . . but lacking the specializations of either the star-fish or vertebrate groups. From these forms, by the assumption of radial symmetry and a sessile mode of life, came the echinoderms. But from these forms, too, seem to have arisen types which retained their original bilateral symmetry . . . From this line, we believe, came the chordates and finally the vertebrates.*

It is certain that the Echinoderms and the Chordates are closely related; but whether the one is ancestral to the other, or whether they are both branches of an earlier stem, are questions that may never be answered beyond dispute.

THE CHORDATE DESIGN

In rocks of Middle Palaeozoic age, the fossil of a small bilateral animal has been found which is known as Jamoytius. The period is far too late for Jamoytius itself to have been an ancestor of the vertebrates, which by that time were already numerous and varied; but it looks like an early sketch of the Chordate design; and it is probably a member of a surviving line, that had changed very little over a long period. Equally curious is the fact that this line has continued; and it is represented at the present day, only slightly altered, by the lancelet. In the lancelet, therefore, we see a living creature that must be very close indeed to the lost ancestor of all the vertebrates. It has no

*A. S. Romer, *Man and the Vertebrates*, Penguin Books 1954, p. 16.

backbone; but it has a notocord – the simple rod-like structure from which backbones were evolved.

The lancelet has a slender fish-like shape. Its body is translucent and about two inches long. It spends most of its time partly buried in the sand, waiting for a meal to turn up; but if this should not happen, it can swim very well to a more favourable place. Having slightly flattened sides, and paired blocks of muscle through the length of its body, it is capable of swift, sinuous movement. It is stiffened by a flexible rod – the promise of a backbone – above which lies the nerve-cord. This nerve-cord exemplifies the original ground-plan of the vertebrate nervous system.

In the Coelenterates, the characteristic arrangement of the nervous elements is the nerve-net; but in the Chordates, it is the nerve-cord. The nerve-net is, of course, more primitive. How did it evolve into a cord? Although this cannot be answered in detail, it is evident that the change from radial to bilateral symmetry necessitated a corresponding change in the neural design; and it is *as if* the ancient nerve-net became rolled into a tube, which then ran lengthwise through these new long-bodied animals, with branchings to each part. This tubular shape is the basic notion that one must form of the central nervous system of all animals that have a backbone.

In the lancelet, the neural tube lies above the notocord; but as evolution proceeds, for reasons of security, it gradually sinks into a more protected position. In ourselves, the central nervous system encased in the backbone and the skull, is the most protected of all our organs; and yet, in our own embryological development, it is seen to arise from cells that were at one time on the surface. This is a hint of its history; and in every developing embryo of the lancelet, the opening chapter is re-told.

The first indication is a down-folding of the surface, lengthwise along the back. This furrow deepens, its sides approach, they close over at the top, and the furrow becomes a tube. The cells in the tube-wall then differentiate into nerve-cells and supporting tissue. When the nerve-cells are complete and functioning, it is seen that they are already specialized for their three main duties – to receive information, to assess the situation, and to order the response. Since it takes many cells to do each class of work, they gather into groups; and there gradually form, as thickenings in the wall of the neural tube, all inter-connected, sensory centres, association centres, and motor centres. This, displayed in the simplest of the Chordates, is the groundwork of our central nervous system.

In an animal like the lancelet, which has neither a skull nor a backbone, and only rudimentary special senses, the tubular shape of the central nervous system is as little deformed as it well could be. It is nearly a perfect scroll. But it is not quite regular: there is already a slight expansion at the front-end. This is due to the fact that the front inevitably receives the greatest amount of stimulation, and responds to it by becoming progressively enlarged. Ultimately, this enlargement becomes a brain.

In spite of its gradual retreat to a protected situation, the central nervous system must always keep in touch with every part. The fine outgrowths from its cells, the nerve-fibres, therefore lengthen; and a nerve is a bundle of these slender threads, each carrying its own distinct train of impulses. In the lancelet, pairs of nerves – one sensory and the other motor – enter and leave the nerve-tube at regular intervals. Later, when bone has been evolved, and the spinal cord has become securely encased, strict symmetry is imposed on these pairs by the segments of the vertebral column between which they have to pass. But this has not yet happened in the lancelet, and so they alternate – the motor nerves going directly to the muscle-blocks, and the sensory nerves entering between them. The principle of pairs, however, has been established and remains.

Even at this stage, therefore, we see the elements of a plan that will endure. The paired sensory and motor nerves entering and leaving the cord; the dividing of the sensory fibres into ascending and descending branches inside the cord, which foreshadow the major nervous pathways; the pooling of their information at certain centres; and the general division of the neural tube into an upper part (dorsal) in which the pathways and centres are mainly sensory and correlative, and an under part (ventral) in which they are mainly effectory and motor – all these are structural principles that are still exhibited in us. They were worked out in the Early Palaeozoic seas by the unknown forerunner of Jamoytius – a tiny nervous scroll, on which the symbols of our inner world were beginning to be traced.

THE AGE OF FISHES

In 450,000,000 B.P., which is nearly the mid-point of the Palaeozoic Era, the sea covered most of what is now the State of Colorado. On its coastline there was a shallow bay, receiving the waters of a river, and it is in rocks that were formed in this bay that the earliest fragments of bone have been discovered. They are the defensive scales of primitive fishes – almost certainly fresh-water fishes which inhabited the river. These are the first known animals with a backbone.

After this tantalizing glimpse, there is a long gap in the record; but by 400,000,000 B.P. the evidence of primitive fishes is plentiful, and is found in many parts of the world. By that time, there were numerous species; but all still wore the curious armour from which they have received their name – Ostracoderms, the shell-skinned. It is to be supposed that their armour was a protection against the Eurypterids, which also dwelt in fresh water and had become quite formidable.

If the shell-skinned fishes had been stripped of this covering, they would have been very like a modern lamprey. Casts of their brains and other internal parts show that the lamprey is their lineal descendant, and that except for the loss of armour and the degeneration of its bones, it has scarcely altered. Despite their great age, therefore, we can form a clear conception not only of the appearance but also of the bodily workings of the Ostracoderms.

They had round, sucking mouths with which they grubbed a living from the river-bottoms; and to become true fishes, they needed jaws and fins. The jaws developed first, by the gradual conversion of the front pair of gill-arches. The earliest jaws were not very efficient, and the group that evolved them became extinct; but before doing so, it gave rise to a line that led on to the true fishes – with perfected jaws and teeth. This was a decisive innovation, which brought the long dominion of the Arthropods to an end; and with this new means of defence and aggression, the fishes were able to leave the river-bottoms. Some ventured into the sea, and slowly their cumbrous armour was shed. It has not, however, vanished without trace; and 'almost every element in the human skull can be directly compared with a corresponding element in the skull of these ancient bony fishes.'*

Well-controlled movement at varying depths required fins for steering and steadying the body. Arising from flaps of skin, fins passed through an experimental phase and then settled into a pattern – single fins on the back and tail, and two pairs on the underside of the body. The lower pairs – the pectoral and pelvic fins – are of particular interest, because they are the starting-points of arms and legs. Originally, they were used for stabilization in the water; but some of the new genera of fishes – the less fortunate probably – went back to life on the river-bottoms, and they found these paired appendages useful for crawling. In a few species – the Crossopterygians – they became strengthened with a framework of bone. The pattern of these fin-bones, known from many fossils, can be followed in unbroken development to the human leg and foot, arm and hand.

These bottom-crawlers came to be faced with a survival problem. They lived in an age of continental uplift and retreating seas, and in many parts of the world there was severe seasonal drought. As lakes and ponds shrank, even when they did not dry up altogether, they became brackish. There was no longer enough free oxygen in the water to sustain life, and their inhabitants began to die of suffocation. Just above the surface there was unlimited free oxygen, but to make use of it required a special adaptation – the rudiments of lungs. Some of the Crossopterygians achieved this, and became able to rise to the surface and gulp air; and some of their lineal descendants, living under similar conditions in parts of Australia, Africa and South America, still use an air-breathing organ that has not greatly changed. These modern lung-fishes are a fascinating survival from one of the most critical periods of evolution.

The beginnings of legs and lungs were acquired in the water, and the fishes that possessed them may be said to have been pre-adapted to life on land. When further climatic stress was imposed on them, some were able to make the momentous change. During the millions of years that they spent in the water, members of this group were conspicuously unsuccessful. They lived in conditions of adversity; and compared with their cousins who had taken to the sea, and who were then multiplying, diversifying and filling the oceans, they were a miserable,

*A. S. Romer, *Man and the Vertebrates*, Penguin Books 1954, p. 26.

depauperated lot. This was a harsh schooling; but it was necessary, because their future lay in the conquest of a new element and in a more arduous way of life. In the Age of Fishes, one might say, there were fine fish and poor fish; and it is from the poor fish that all the land-vertebrates descend.

THE BRAIN BENEATH THE WATER

While no one would belittle the importance of legs and lungs, the most remarkable contribution that the fishes made to land-life was their brains. If we ask what kind of brain the first land-vertebrates brought with them from the water, and how much we ourselves inherit from river, lake and sea, the answer is that the central nervous system of these early fishes had nearly all the broad features, structural and functional, that are found in us. Almost four hundred million years of development has intervened, and yet the fundamental pattern has not altered. It was, of course, much simpler; but it can be described, to a remarkable extent, in the same anatomical terms.

Although the old anatomists who invented these terms had but a vague idea of the brain's functions, they had formed a good picture of its structure; and the names they gave to its principle parts are still in use. Their language was descriptive, rich in pictorial analogy, and to the layman, at least, this is pleasing. From a fancied resemblance to a little sea-horse, an area of the forebrain was named the hippocampus, the 'sea-monster'; between the forebrain and the midbrain is the thalamus, the 'secret chamber'; there are the four 'little hills', the 'bridge', the 'almond' and the 'pear'; the outer layers are the 'bark' or cortex; and finally, woven in the last phase of its evolution is the neopallium, the 'new garment'.

Some scientists now find this irritating, and would prefer a functional terminology borrowed from the engineer; but it is surely a good thing that a place should be left for poetry in our conception of the brain's mysterious operations. Mechanics are not enough. What is the little 'sea-monster' really doing? He does the work of a computer; but he is something more than that; he is also part of the foundations of a mind, contributing in a small degree to the creations of an inner world. If he were not there, the rose might smell less sweet, and Shakespeare would have lost a metaphor. To rename him as one piece of a homeostat would be no less inadequate than to say that he is part of a poem. In some strange manner he is both; for a brain does more than ensure the survival of a body; it serves also to create a world of thought, imagination and art which, in due time, exists and is valued for itself. A purely mechanical terminology might incline us to forget that biosphere and psychosphere have evolved together.

The primary duty of a nervous system, however, is to guide the responses of a physical body; and to do so efficiently, it must enable – indeed compel – the organism to respond as a unit. Disaster would follow if the parts behind cried, Forward!, and those in front cried, Back! And what prevents this from happening is the integrative function of the nervous system. To perform this function, it must itself be a unit from the beginning, and remain one throughout its evolution. However complex it may gradually become, this imposes a certain design – one in which functionally related cells form centres with a network of correlating fibres between them.

The topography of the cell-groups, the detail of the design, is a consequence of the impulses that reach them. It is by them that the evolving pattern is shaped. The dendrites grow *towards* the source of stimulation, and carry the impulse from it into the cell; the axons grow *away* from the source of stimulation – which in their case is the cell-body – and so carry the impulse onwards. It is this dynamic polarization which determines the growth of the nerve-endings and ultimately causes the migration of cells into nervous centres. The outcome is the permanent association of those cells and cell-groups that are habitually brought into activity at the same time and from the same cause.

The final cause lies in the outer world, because it is by stimuli from without that the nerve-impulse is first aroused: the evolving pattern within is thus shaped by the environment, and in a sense contains it as a dynamic symbol. When special receptor organs have been evolved for the special senses – smelling, seeing, hearing – they will accordingly create, and not merely possess, corresponding nervous centres conveniently situated in the central system. We have seen the nerve-net become a scroll; and we have now to witness the transformation of this scroll, the old nerve-cord, under the influence of these forces. This process is the creation of a brain.

The first Chordates, on the pattern of the lancelet, had only one organ of special sense – a small pit at the front, sensitive to smell. Corresponding to it, was a slight enlargement at the tip of the neural tube; this marks the germinal point of the forebrain. The ancient fishes, however, were far more discerning. They had evolved eyes, served by pairs of nerve-centres a little further back; and this second expansion of the walls of the neural tube is the origin of the midbrain. They also had special receptors sensitive to vibration, including sound; and their counterparts in the central system form the hindbrain. Beyond this point, the modifications were comparatively minor. From the evolutionary stage of the fishes, therefore, we must picture the central nervous system as the spinal cord culminating in a triple brain.

Originally, the forebrain was for smelling, the midbrain for seeing, and the hindbrain for the senses that were left over. In animals with paired limbs and sense-organs, the brain naturally developed a corresponding bilateral symmetry. When the smelling organ of the first Chordates was duplicated, so, in consequence, was the forebrain; and in the fishes, the front end of the neural tube looks like a pair of hollow buds. These seem insignificant in the fishes; but they have a great future in land-animals, for they are the beginning of the cerebral hemispheres.

During embryological development, the manner in which the duplication of the forebrain arose can be clearly seen. In what was at first a single cavity, upfoldings from the middle of the floor are met by downfoldings from the middle of the roof. A partition is thus formed, creating two U-shaped chambers, each of which keeps a narrow opening into the neural canal. Although the upfolds and the downfolds unite as a middle wall, they retain their distinction – the septum below, and the hippocampus, the domain of the little 'sea-horse', above. Facing them on the outside walls of the hemispheres, other characteristic thickenings develop: the upper is the 'pear' (pyriform formation), and the lower is the 'almond' (amygdaloid formation). There is still nothing much in the roof; but in land-life, this will be marvellously elaborated, and in the mammalian brain, it will ultimately dominate the whole.

Leading from the forebrain to the midbrain, is the 'secret

chamber', the thalamus. As the importance of the forebrain increases, the walls of the thalamus come to accommodate the relay centres where impulses, ascending and descending, are received and re-addressed. This is of no great importance in the fishes; because in them, the midbrain is the predominant part. On its roof, symmetrically placed on either side, are two little domes – the optic lobes; and at this level of evolution, nearly all the nerve-fibres from the eyes end here. They are the visual centres. In land-animals, this arrangement is gradually changed, and the optic fibres are diverted to the forebrain. Ages will pass before this highway is completed; but even in the fishes, the beginnings of the track are there. As more and more fibres are gradually diverted to it, new visual centres are created in the hemispheres, while the old ones dwindle. A fish is blinded by an injury to the midbrain, but a man is not.

The optic lobes of the fishes exhibit, in comparative simplicity, principles of construction that are of great importance. The fibres coming from the eyes enter at the top, spread out superficially, and then branch downwards into a layer of very small cells. The function of these small cells is to interpret the impulses they receive, and then to send the appropriate orders, other impulses, to a layer of large cells which underlies them. These have long axons which discharge into motor centres and so effect the muscular response. This basic layer-sequence or lamination – the fibres of delivery, the small correlating cells, and the large effector cells – is found in other parts of the brain where the same kind of work has to be done; and although much complicated it is still the fundamental structure of the mammalian forebrain.

At the level of the fishes, it would seem as if the midbrain can do almost everything, in a simpler manner, that the forebrain takes over later. It is here that fishes learn. It is also their general co-ordinating area, and tracts reach it from other brain-parts bringing information from other senses. To put sense and sense together is the foundation of the ability to put two and two together. It is the activity of a mind.

The hindbrain is the third and last enlargement of the original neural tube, and arose in connection with the remaining senses – taste, touch, vibration, balance. All the cranial nerves except the olfactory and the optic arise from the hindbrain. It tapers at the back, and merges with the spinal cord, which is the least modified part of the vertebrate nervous system.

If we had been able to look beneath the skull of the Cross-opterygians, this triple brain-form would have been clearly discernible. Beneath the human skull, we find the convoluted surface of the hemispheres – the 'distracted orb' of man; but this visible part is the new brain, the neopallium, which in the course of mammalian evolution has gradually enveloped the old. It is an expansion of the hemispheres and now conceals the ancient pattern that the first land-vertebrates brought with them from the water. That, none the less, is the foundation on which our superstructure has been built; and in these three brain-parts – originally sensory divisions – that fraction of the universe to which we are able to respond, or to be conscious of, is mysteriously symbolized.

CRACKING THE CODE

It is characteristic of the receptor cells that they respond to one mode of energy and to no other. In consequence, they analyse the environment; and on the basis of this information, the nerve cells perform a new synthesis. The receptors might be compared with transducers – a transducer being a device which is activated by waves from one medium and supplies related waves to another. On this analogy, 'waves' from the varied media of the outer world are transduced by the receptors into a single type of electrical 'wave' – the nerve-impulse. This is the first step towards the new synthesis. The many forms of outside energy are reduced to one, which is the same throughout the whole nervous system. As this applies to all the senses, it may be illustrated in terms of sight.

From the surrounding world of objects, light is reflected in a pattern which their surfaces impose. This pattern of wave-particles constitutes a natural 'code', which, if there were any means of 'cracking the code', would impart some information about the nature of the reflecting objects. For the most part, it is not interpreted and streams out into the void; but an infinitesimal fraction of this patterned light is sometimes intercepted by an eye. The retina of the eye is a fixed arrangement of sensitive cells, each of which responds characteristically to the bombardment of the light-quanta it receives. It does so by the absorption of the quanta, which then initiate a chemical reaction. The retinal effect – the so-called retinal image – is not therefore a passive reflection, but a scintillating pattern of activity. Groups of retinal cells are connected with an individual optic fibre; and the summated activity of the group sets up a train of impulses in the fibre. So far as the optic fibres are concerned, this means that each one of them carries exclusively the experience or information of its own group of retinal cells.

The 'light code' of the outer world has thus been translated into an inner 'neural code'; but there is still a point-to-point transmission – as there was from points on the surface of the object seen to points on the retina responding; because every fibre carries its distinct train of signals from and to a definite place. In ourselves, there are about a million fibres in each optic nerve, and perhaps a hundred and twenty million retinal cells to supply them. In the simple forms we have been considering, there were, of course, far less; but the principle is still the same, point-to-point from eye to brain, so that in the case of the fishes the retina is mapped, or pointilistically represented, in the optic tectum. If some wavering 'image' arises there, in the darkness of the brain, it is evident that this must be purely symbolic. Visual perception involves the attribution of meaning to this dark neural symbol, and interprets it in terms of an outer world of light.

So it is with the other senses. We hear a certain tone because the brain-cells are excited in a certain place. The nerve-impulses themselves are indistinguishable; and whether they are translated as a sight, a sound, a pain, or any other kind of perception is determined by the pathways they have travelled on and the precise locality in the brain at which they arrive. Any excitation of the visual or auditory centres 'means' seeing or hearing; and if they are stimulated in some abnormal way, there will still be an experience of sight or sound even if it has no counterpart in the outer world; normally, however, the brain-event is the result of an external event, and constitutes a new synthesis by which the world is recreated symbolically in each perceiving mind.

What must be stressed, therefore, is the importance of locality. Our thoughts may wander, but our brain-cells do not. The cells form a fixed frame of reference, and what wanders are the ripples of excitement that constitute perception and thought; and it is not *what* it is, but *where* it is that gives to each ripple its meaning.

How this pattern of electro-chemical activity is translated into precise experiences of seeing, hearing, touching and pain – which, of course, involve consciousness – presents a problem at least as great as that of the creation of the pattern itself; but because the process by which the physical fact becomes the psychical experience is so elusive, we are inclined to forget how stupendous the achievement really is. The neural code has been elaborated slowly throughout the whole course of zoological evolution, and it could not have been cracked suddenly when it had already reached a complexity that defies analysis. If, as is sometimes asserted, consciousness arose rather late in evolution, then the cracking of the code would have been a pure miracle. If that did happen, there is no rational explanation of perception, and we may place its advent wherever we like. We may say, if we choose, the birds and the mammals have it, the fishes and the amphibia have not; but this is merely arbitrary. Reason asserts that the attribution of meaning to the symbolic pattern could have been made only as the pattern itself took shape, step-by-step with the building of the nervous system; and there is no place, within the sphere of reason, for a mindless zoology.

THE LAND

It is said that Confucius was once asked to sum up his philosophy in a single word, and that he answered, 'Perhaps reciprocity would do.' The study of evolution suggests a similar concept. When some living-space is taken over by new inhabitants, both are changed; and reciprocity is a determinant of such changes. The outcome is not a static, planned creation, but continuous, mutual creation.

Between three and four hundred million years ago, a new pattern of creative relationships began to take shape, because a group of fishes, that had long been unfortunate in their original environment, ventured into a new one, and put their remarkable pre-adaptations of crawling and breathing to an unprecedented use. It was by the demands of this new environment, the land, that their future was determined; and so it is this setting, the Earth's continental features, that we must now consider.

In the sea, there are no abrupt changes; as an environment, it is rather stable and uniform; but it is characteristic of the land that there are violent contrasts and constant variations. Life must adapt to them or perish; and the history of any corner of the Earth, wherever we may happen to live, will illustrate these stupendous transformations.

The British Isles, for example, have been almost completely buried under an ice-cap that has left its mark as far south as the Thames. They have been many times invaded by the sea, one testimony of which is the chalk cliffs of Dover, formed by the accumulation of minute marine shells. They have been a Sahara, with scattered oases, where sandstones were laid down by a desert wind. They have been a steaming, tropical jungle, which finally decayed into seams of coal. They have been the scene of violent volcanism, when lavas were erupted over hundreds of square miles. They have been part of a chain of mountains, of Himalayan grandeur, which stretched from Wales and Ireland to the north of Norway; and they have been the bed of a coral sea. Recorded in their rocks is the whole succession of evolving life. These glimpses of bewildering change are not unique: they are representative, and can be matched in other parts of the Earth. But how is it possible to account for vicissitudes so numerous and so extreme?

The causes of some of them may be extra-planetary. Changes in solar radiation, it has been suggested, may have been partly responsible for periodic glaciations that at times have covered even the sun-scorched deserts of Australia; the general expansion of the universe may have local effects; and it is possible that the supposed constants of physics are not constant over vast spans of time. But the main causes of the Earth's unrest lie in itself. The surface movements, the uplift and subsidence of continents and the building of mountain chains, are determined in the impenetrable depths.

Less awe-inspiring, but very effective in the course of time, are the agencies that are easily observed. Frost, rain, wind, chemistry – by their simple, slow, but ceaseless, activities the rocks are split and worn away. It needs only time for a mountain-range to disappear. Before the fossil-record began six hundred million years ago, the Earth had already passed through at least nine periods of mountain-building. Ranges as great as any of today had been upraised, eroded, and levelled into plains.

The particular changes through which the British Isles have passed are due to the fact that all Europe, except the Baltic Shield, was once part of a very unstable area which was progressively consolidated in the three mountain-building epochs – orogenies is the geological term – that have occurred since the beginning of the Palaeozoic Era. These appear to have affected the whole planet, and were separated from each other by intervals of about two hundred million years. They are known as the Caledonian, the Hercynian, and the Alpine movements.

In Europe they created three mountain-systems, each rising to the south of its forerunner. The Caledonian and Hercynian chains are now mere vestiges, and even the Alps have lost something of their youthful stature. Each of these orogenic movements resulted in a different geography – the Old Red Sandstone Continent, the Hercynian Continent, and finally, with the birth of the Alps, the Europe that we know.

When the mountains were at their highest and the seas in retreat, climates were most extreme, and were severely testing to every form of life. These were the periods of mass-extinction, and are turning-points in biological change. As the ranges were weathered and worn down, the landscape changed to lowlands, then to swamps and marshes, and finally to lagoons and intrusive seas. The climate at these periods was equable, moist, and usually hot. So it happens that the sub-tropical forests that have left the coal measures flourished between the Old Red Sandstone and the New, and that the Great Chalk Sea spread from southern England to the Ural Mountains when the Hercynian Continent had been worn away. The prelude to the uplift of new mountains is a period of tremendous volcanism; and so one may discern a certain regularity, a rhythmic pulsation, giving intelligible order to what seems at first a mere confusion of stupendous change.

Although volcanism and mountain-building are the most spectacular of the Earth's activities, the slow rise and fall of vast areas have been even more important to life, because they determine the retreats and invasions of the continental seas. The reasons for them are not fully understood. Some vertical movements are only readjustments of the crust to a redistribution of weight. The formation of an ice-cap may cause the crust to sink, and there are areas in the Baltic that show a steady rise due to their still-continuing recovery from bearing the load of the Ice Age. When a mountain-chain is eroded, an enormous weight is removed, and the mountain-roots may be lifted to the point of rejuvenating the chain. There are also more mysterious forces at work, arising from movements in the Earth's mantle. But whatever their causes, slow, widespread uplifts and subsidences, with consequent regressions and transgressions of the sea, are a recurring theme in Earth-history. They are not events by which to be dumbfounded, like Noah's flood: they are to be expected of the Earth, like the rhythmic breathing of a living thing.

CONTINENTS AND MOUNTAINS

A continent is the last and lightest solid product of the process of geochemical differentiation, which means that it is basically a thin, irregular slab of granitic rock. It is solid because it has cooled, and it is on the top because it is light. The basaltic layer it rests on is not only denser, but also so much hotter in places that it is yielding or molten. When a continent is pictured in this way – as a floating raft of granite – there seems to be no reason why it should always remain in the same place.

These generalities are agreed, but there is still no agreement on how the continents were formed. According to one view, they are the remnants of a world-encircling shell; according to another, now prevalent, they have grown by accretion around nuclei known as shields; but as they are certainly platforms of granite resting on denser rock, the process of granitization is one key to their origin. There are many kinds of granite, however, and they have been formed in different ways and at different times. Granite is a rock that has once been molten; but upper, sedimentary rocks may sink to levels that are very hot, where they are fused and melted into new granites that are afterwards extruded. It is virtually certain that all known granites have been thus re-worked, and that no part of the Earth's original crust remains for our inspection.

Although their origins are obscure, there is now good

Brightly coloured, scented flowers, to attract insects & ensure pollination.

Flowering trees & grasses: true flowers & enclosed seeds: generally wind-pollinated.

Cone bearers: primitive flowers: the first seeds.

Ferns, horsetails & clubmosses: no flowers nor seeds, but true roots, stems & leaves. Some of them bear spores in cones.

Liverworts: no flowers nor seeds: no true roots nor stems. Mosses: simple roots and water-conducting stems.

Algae, fungi, lichens: no flowers nor seeds: no roots, stems nor leaves.

The Evolution of the Plants (*Messrs P. R. Gawthorn Ltd.*)

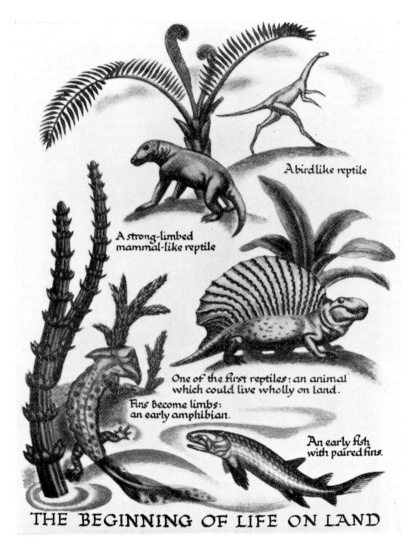

The Beginning of Life on Land (*Messrs P. R. Gawthorn Ltd.*)

evidence that vast land-masses have split and that the portions have become separated. Until recently, this was a controversial question; and Du Toit, who has for long been a proponent of continental drift, once wrote sarcastically of the 'dumbfounding spectacle of the present continental masses, firmly anchored to a plastic foundation, yet remaining fixed in space!'* And in place of this unnatural oddity, he assumed a restless, pulsating Earth with all its parts in relative motion. But what forces could move a continent?

It is surmised that the most important of them are convection currents in the Earth's mantle. The mantle is not liquid, but it is sufficiently hot for its substance, in the course of ages, gradually to flow. The super-heated material at the bottom tends to rise, and the cooler material at the top tends to sink. In this way, circulating currents are set up, very slow-moving, but comparable with those in a kettle of water on a stove. These are convection currents; and although it is extremely difficult to calculate their behaviour in the Earth's mantle, it is evident that they might be the cause of various crustal movements that seem otherwise mysterious. The slow rise and fall of huge land-masses is one such movement, continental drift is another, and mountain-building is a third.

Mountain-building presents a number of problems, and not all of them have been solved. The first fact that must be accounted for is that the rocks that form the mountains were laid down beneath the sea. Wherever there is now a great mountain-system there was once a marine trough, which filled slowly with the sediments since lifted to the mountain-crests. This is explained by the theory of geosynclines, which is one of the most important concepts in geology. A geosyncline might be thought of as the womb from which the mountains emerge, and an orogeny as the labour of their birth.

At its beginning, a geosyncline is a very long submarine valley, or string of submarine basins, bordering a stable land-mass. In some cases it is placed between two neighbouring masses. Its chief characteristic is the weakness of its floor; in fact it is a belt of crustal weakness, which may be related to convection currents in the mantle; and as the sediments from the wearing down of adjacent lands are carried into it, the bottom sags beneath the growing weight. The sea above is

*A. L. Du Toit, *Our Wandering Continents*, Oliver & Boyd 1937, p. 3.

never deep; but the filling of sedimentary rock, slowly subsiding, becomes very profound.

Over long time-spans – tens of millions of years – the down-warp may come to be as much as forty thousand feet; and long before this depth is reached, pressure and heat have begun to transform the sedimentary rocks. These are the regions of metamorphism, where, for example, limestone is converted into marble. At still lower levels, the rocks are melted and new granites are formed. It is some measure of the events that we have now to picture that rocks from these profundities may be uplifted to form the peaks of mountains – the summit of the Matterhorn is made of a crystalline rock that was once molten at such depths.

The subsidence is followed by uplift. We have compared a geosyncline to the womb from which mountains are born; and the Earth's labour is brought on by immense compressional forces, exerting a series of prodigious sideways thrusts. These are not continuous, but occur in mighty spasms, which may be separated by periods, comparatively relaxed, of several million years. What causes these lateral movements? When a geosyncline lies between two continental masses, it is conceivable, if continents move, that they might converge and close on it like the jaws of a vice. As the rocks that fill the geosyncline are younger and less rigid than those by which it is flanked, they fold under the pressure. They rise into low and then into towering ridges, which become faulted, break, and are finally piled on to one another. Most geologists now believe that this is what happened during the three orogenies we have mentioned – the Caledonian, the Hercynian and the Alpine.

Coastal ranges, such as those bordering the Pacific Ocean, require other concepts; but we shall not pursue the question here. The bewildering changes through which the British Isles have passed, and which are matched in other lands, find their most comprehensive explanation in the principle that continents move. And it is vicissitudes such as these that characterize the new environment of danger, promise and unrest to which living things had to adapt themselves when they emerged from the comparatively peaceful waters.

THE OLD GEOGRAPHY

The land-masses of the Earth are at present in two groups, forming an eastern and a western hemisphere; but this was not the case in the Palaeozoic World. The Atlantic Ocean did not then exist; and the main land-groups were north and south, separated by a central sea out of which the Alpine-Himalayan mountain-system afterwards arose. This sea, although bridged occasionally by emergent land, is one of the main features of ancient geography; and for the greater part of the last thousand million years it has provided a marine thoroughfare from the Far East to the Far West, reaching the single ocean at both extremities. It has been named after the ancient goddess, wife of Oceanus and mother of the Oceanides, the Tethys.

South of the Tethys there was an immense continent – Gondwanaland. It comprised what is now South America, Africa, India, Australia and Antarctica. It is now generally agreed that Gondwanaland was a continent that fractured, and of which the pieces have drifted to their present situations. Their former unity is shown by the stratification of their rocks, the history of their glaciations, and their fossils. The process of fragmentation has not ceased, and the Great Rift Valley is an indication of the gradual break-up of Africa.

North of the Tethys there was an inter-related group of three immense islands – representing the nuclei of North America, Europe and Northern Asia. They were parted by two geosynclinal seas, belts of mobility where the most momentous geological manifestations were to be enacted. From one of these seas, the Caledonian Mountains emerged in the Palaeozoic, and from the other, the Ural Mountains in the Mesozoic Era. The Tethys itself, much later, was to be the womb of the Alps and the Himalayas.

THE OLD RED SANDSTONE CONTINENT

Geography changes to an appreciable extent even in a few centuries: the Palaeozoic Era lasted some three hundred and seventy-five million years. It is evident, therefore, that a picture of its physical features can be only an outline: the details of palaeogeography will never be known. Such a broad impression of the Early Palaeozoic world would include a tripartite northern land-mass split by two geosynclines, the Caledonian and the Uralian. Most of the British Isles were then submerged. They were, in fact, part of the Caledonian geosyncline, which extended approximately from the south of Ireland to the north of Norway. During the Age of Fishes, a series of tremendous movements of compression and uplift converted this submarine valley into a mountain-system. This was the Caledonian orogeny. It gave rise to a chain comparable with the present Himalayas, and welded all the land from Canada to Russia into a single continent.

The backbone of the ancient Caledonian Mountains was the Ireland to Norway line; but a second chain branched from the main one in Scotland, following a south-easterly curve across and beyond what is now the North Sea. Although no orogeny can be exactly dated, the main movements of compression and upthrust took place about 400,000,000 B.P.; and it was the subsequent wearing-down of these mountains by rain, rivers and wind that formed the Old Red Sandstone from which the vanished continent has received its name.

At the beginning of its history, this vast new land was dominated by youthful ranges, vibrant with active volcanoes. Its climate was hot, and in places arid. Violent storms washed the products of erosion to the plains, where they were taken up by the wind and swept into drifts and dunes often thousands of feet thick. These aeolian deposits of many-coloured sands, mostly red, are its characteristic geological remains.

In the rivers, lakes and coastal waters of this immense island, there was varied and abundant life; but the land itself, although not entirely barren, was harsh and forbidding. It was a challenge to life. And in this lies the drama of the Old Red Continent – that it began with sandy wastes and it ended with woodlands. This invasion took a long time; and before the victory of the trees, the Caledonian Mountains had been worn away.

THE FIRST LAND-PLANTS

Until fairly recently it was thought that no land-plants existed in the Early Palaeozoic, but spores of this period have now been found in the Baltic countries and in Siberia. The discovery is not surprising. The first well-known land-flora, dating from the middle of the era, is only relatively primitive: it had solved the fundamental problems of land-living, and its species were already diverse. It must have had a long line of predecessors, although their character remains obscure.

The passage of life from sea to land was by the way of diminishing waters – river, lake, pond, mud. At least it is certain that vertebrate animals came to land from fresh water; there is no evidence that the plants did so; and it is possible that marine plants, gently habituated by the ebb and flow of the tides, were the first to survive on land. But it is clear that any form of aquatic life that ventures as far as the stream and the pond will at some time find itself stranded. Only two possibilities then remain – to die or to become adapted to air.

Long before any plants lived on land, however, there had been 'forests' in the sea. Red, brown, and blue-green algae were the first living things to attain any considerable size; and for a long time, in what is sometimes called the Age of Sea-weeds, they were the only ones to do so. They developed large leaf-like forms, through which light-energy was absorbed and chemical exchanges took place. Life had been easy for them in the sea. There had been no danger of desiccation, the water had given them support, and their sex-cells had been simply shed into it and fertilization left to chance encounter.

The water had been a friendly element, but the air was not. It gave no help in any of these ways; indeed, it was hostile. To survive in it required a new covering to protect the plant from drying up, a stiffening of its fabric so that it could stand alone, and, the most stubborn problem of all, a new method of reproduction. As animals could not live on land until the plants had made it habitable, their further evolution had to wait until these difficulties had been surmounted.

The reproductive problem was the most recalcitrant; and the first land-plants, like the first land-animals, were amphibian.

This was a great impediment to their expansion. The simplest way of producing a new individual is, of course, by the repeated division of a single cell; and a cell especially set aside for this purpose in a complex organism is a spore. Spores are sufficient for reproduction; but to obtain a diversified population the uniting of cells from different parents and the sharing of their potentialities is required. It is necessary, also, that one of these cells should contain a store of nourishment for the developing embryo; and consequently a distinction arose between the male and female sex-cells – the sperm and the egg. The egg is larger, because it contains food, and it is comparatively immobile. The sperm is active and in perpetual quest: it must find the egg or die.

Water-plants had discovered all these principles before life on land began, and some of the commonest seaweeds exemplify them still. One might fancy that they had adopted sex reluctantly, as if they did not fully trust it, and that this indecision led to their curious reproductive cycle of alternating generations. One generation produces spores, but the plants that arise from it produce sex-cells; their offspring return to spores, and so on alternately.

This half-hearted participation in reproductive progress worked well in the water; but to adapt it to land was very difficult, because the male cell knew of no way to reach the female except by water. It might swim to it or drift, but without water it could not travel at all. The first land-plants, therefore, had to be amphibian. The greater part of their life-cycle could be passed on dry ground, but it was only in water that their sex-cells could unite; and although a thin film might be sufficient, this effectively confined them to damp or marshy places.

The full solution of this problem was not found until late in the Mesozoic Era. It is a flower. If the plants first came to land at the beginning of the Palaeozoic, then it took them about five hundred million years to work out this perfect answer; and to understand why they required so long, one must appreciate their difficulties. At the outset, they were placed in a dilemma. To be sure of water for their reproduction, it was an advantage to be close to the ground: to obtain light-energy for their other activities, and to disseminate their spores, it was an advantage to grow tall and to spread their branches widely.

The ultimate solution was for the male cells to outgrow their dependence on water and to become a wind-born pollen; but that lay in the distant future, and entailed many other changes that were not easily made. Meanwhile, they invented a provisional method, which was so satisfactory in damp places that it is still used by the ferns. This accentuated the difference between the alternate generations: the sexual generation was reduced to a tiny plantlet, which had no purpose in life but to produce its sex-cells close to the moist earth in circumstances that permitted them to meet; but the spore-bearing generation grew up into a tall, leafy, conspicuous plants. Ages afterwards, when wind had taken the place of water for the transportation of the male cells, the sexual generation was retained on the plant. It became the flower.

The earliest well known land-flora is Middle Palaeozoic, and was similar throughout the world. Its remains have been found in Australia, Europe, and North America. By the combined chances of preservation and discovery, its classic locality is Scotland; and the most abundant of these vanished plants – Rhynia – is named after the village of Rhynie in Aberdeenshire. At that time, the Caledonian chain had already been much reduced and this district was a marsh.

These plants, which have been preserved in minute detail, were neither large nor beautiful; but they were the forerunners of life in a new sphere. No animal could venture on to land until there were verdant pathways; and well before this age, they had been slowly extending. Beneath the barren magnificence of the Caledonian Mountains, in valley and lowland, there must have been many threads and patches of green.

This Old Red Sandstone flora looks like the mere bones of vegetation. It is as if the plants were developing from the skeleton outwards. Their main requirement, if they were to do more than creep, was a stem through which water could be raised, food and energy flow, and by which they could be self-supporting. The first 'naked plants' were not much more than that. Their stems continued underground, foreshadowing roots; they bore side-shoots sparingly, a promise of leaves and branches; and they carried spore-cases at their tips. Their ancestors had been tiny water-plants, but their descendants were the forests.

WOODLANDS AND AMPHIBIANS

Every part of the Earth has experienced dumbfounding changes of climate. What is now the Far North was once a warm and genial land, and it has several times been the birthplace of new forms of life. Nothing except the wandering of continents can account for this. It is not only a question of temperature, but also of light. At these latitudes in winter there is darkness; and yet it would seem to have been from the region of Greenland that, at a much later date, the flowering plants set out upon their conquest of the south. It is in Greenland that the earliest land-vertebrates are known to have lived. And in the latter days of the Old Red Continent, there was a flora in this now-desolate region which was ancestral to that of the Forest Age. It is perhaps thirty million years younger than that of the Rhynie marshes, and shows a great advance on the almost-leafless branch-systems that we have so far described.

This flora was not confined to the Far North, but it flourished there; and in Ellesmere Land, which at present is almost the most northerly land in the world, rich plant-beds have been found. It was approximately at this time that the three main groups which came to dominate the Coal Forests – the ancient club mosses, horsetails, and ferns – first reached the stature of trees; and all of them grew abundantly, with many lesser plants, on the shores of a then-kindly ocean which is now a wilderness of ice.

These were the world's first woodlands – 'the advanced guard of hosts destined to wander over the northern hemisphere and furnish the forests of the Coal Age with a vegetation far more varied and luxuriant.'* Every plant in them would have seemed strange to us, but there were hints of the familiar. The ancient 'club mosses' had something of the look of monkey-puzzle trees, but they were not so large; their upper branches were clothed with long, narrow leaves, disposed in spirals; and cone-shaped clusters of spore-bearing leaves hung from the ends of their slender twigs. The 'horsetails' had tall, jointed stems which forked into up-pointing branches, en-

*A. C. Seward, *Plant Life through the Ages*, Cambridge University Press, 1931, p. 150.

circled by whorls of foliage arranged in tiers. The fernlike plants, of the larger sort, rose unbranching for thirty or forty feet to the summit, and then opened into a wide dome or parasol. Their drooping frondage was a fine filigree of leaflets recalling the tracery of a maidenhair fern. All of these plants were evergreens, not yet colour-splashed with flowers, and their little leaves created the verdure of an endless spring.

It was in these woodlands, the first sylvan setting of the Earth, that animals with backbones emerged from the water. A long period of crawling on the river-bottoms had developed their pectoral and pelvic fins into a foreshadowing of legs; and slow habituation to life in brackish pools included the ability to rise to the surface and take oxygen from the air. In these vital respects, some of the vertebrates were pre-adapted to the land. Fishes so endowed were common in the age of the Rhynie flora and their fossils are plentiful.

The remains of the first true amphibians have been found on the east coast of Greenland, and are more or less contemporary with the Ellesmere plants. Somewhere on the Old Red Continent, therefore, the decisive steps were taken that brought the vertebrates permanently to land. It may be that the complete evidence lies buried beneath the present Greenland ice-cap and will never be known to us. But the transition is comprehensible, and not difficult to reconstruct.

Some parts of the great continent were subject to heavy seasonal rains and long intervals of drought. In these regions, many a watercourse was periodically reduced to a string of pools in which the fishes were trapped. When the smaller pools dried completely, most of their inhabitants died; and rocks containing fossil collections that bear witness to such events have been described as 'platforms of sudden death'. The larger pools, however, might persist until the next rainfall, and some of the stranded air-breathing fishes might crawl to them if they were not too far away. Mutations that made this journey easier would be favoured by natural selection; and so gradually the 'double life', partly in water and partly on land, which is characteristic of amphibians, came to be established in a progressive line. And amphibian, as Romer put it, 'is little more than a peculiar type of fish that is capable of walking on land.'* And it began to walk, not from any wish to explore this

*A. S. Romer, *Man and the Vertebrates*, Penguin Books 1954, p. 52.

unfriendly ground, but in order to return to the refreshing waters.

As the ability to survive on land increased, these journeys would have become more leisurely and potentially much longer. What began as a desperate obstacle-race became a promenade. Those who could linger in the woodlands, then evolving into forests, would have found them much safer than the over-populated pools. No enemies yet lurked among the trees. Some of the Arthropods had long been established there; but they were not dangerous – in fact, they were a source of food. And the land that had once repelled began to beckon.

The amphibians were faced, however, with a reproductive problem very like that of the early plants: their eggs could be fertilized and develop only in the water. Although land-living may now have seemed pleasant to them, they had to return to their pools and rivers to breed. The plants required a seed, and the animals a land-egg, to complete their conquests. The first seeds were being evolved at about this time, but eggs with shells still belonged to the remote future. This did not greatly hamper the early amphibians; because they had ample living-space, no dangerous rivals, and they came in a period when mountains were being degraded and there were increasing expanses of well-watered or swampy ground. After an arduous beginning, they were entering on a long age when the Earth would be favourable to their way of life.

Diversification and radial evolution were the natural consequence. The amphibians never approached the phantasy of the dinosaurs, or the variety of the mammals; but in the days when the world was theirs, some species grew to the size of a small crocodile. Such was Eryops, a variety that was fairly plentiful towards the end of the Palaeozoic Era. Eryops was about six feet in length, with strong but sprawling legs, a large head, and probably spent its time almost equally between land and water. Such forms have long been extinct, and the only amphibians that now survive are small and unimportant – the frogs, the newts, and the salamanders. All these have become very specialized; but the salamander still has the look of a Palaeozoic animal, and one can easily conceive how it emerged from the fish and gave rise to the lizard-form. Such were our ancestors in the forest age that followed the break-up of the Old Red Sandstone Continent.

THE AGE OF TREES

The succession of rocks over much of the northern hemisphere shows the Old Red Sandstone overlaid by marine limestones, then come the Coal Measures, and above them the New Red Sandstone. The successive pictures that this raises in the mind are those of a continent, a shallow sea, a low-lying, steamy forest, and then a new arid continent. The two continents were largely due to the wearing-down of two mountain systems – the Caledonian and the Hercynian. Mountains, lowlands, an islanded sea, then lowlands again, and new mountains. The whole vast span of time, something in the order of a hundred and fifty million years, is thus seen to be dominated by two orogenies.

In the age between the mountains, the great northern land-mass was not fundamentally broken up; but the Old Red Continent was in decay. Low ground and shallow water were frequently changing places; and in the depths of the Tethys there were already intimations of a tremendous, but still-distant change. The slow down-warping of the sea-bed under the weight of sediments from the vanishing land had become profound. There followed a period of submarine volcanism and earthquake, and then a folding of the weaker rocks. Long, low islands emerged, foreshadowing new mountains; but millions of years were still to pass before the orogenic climax, when the islands were uplifted in the Armorican and Hercynian chains. This immense interval was a time of swamps and forests, during which the Coal Measures were laid down. One might call it the age between the mountains, or the age of trees.

The great forests then encircled the Earth in a broad, irregular band from North America through Europe to Siberia; and there is said to be enough unmined coal in Siberia to supply the world for centuries. The climate of this belt was equatorial. At the same time, parts of Gondwanaland which are now in or near the tropics were extremely cold, and before the end of the era they were under ice. These climatic facts are beyond dispute, recorded in the rocks, but there is no agreed explanation of them; and in terms of traditional, sober conceptions of the Earth's behaviour, they are inexplicable.

Some climatic changes have been world-wide, and these

might be attributed to an extra-planetary cause; some have been regional, with a pattern that suggests the independent movement of continents; but a tropical zone at the latitude of the British Isles and a simultaneous glaciation in the Southern Hemisphere seems to imply that the whole land-mass of the Earth was at that time displaced to the south, so that the equator passed through Europe and the extremities of Gondwanaland were in the Antarctic. One is therefore obliged to assume, as Lester King has put it, 'the majestic drift of super-continents through the climatic girdles of the Earth.'*

The forest was in its prime about three hundred million years ago; and when the new mountains were born, it died. Its later phases were the most luxuriant. It had trees of giant stature, some of a hundred and twenty feet; but it contained no familiar tree, and to us it would have seemed unearthly. The three groups that had appeared in the earliest woodlands were still predominant; but each had become diversified into many genera and species, and all had evolved some majestic trees. From the club mosses had sprung the giants – the lepidodendrons and sigillarias; from the horsetails had arisen the tall, slender calamites; and the ferns and seed-ferns had grown into a waving multitude of many-patterned fronds.

The lepidodendrons have been called scale-trees, because of the curious pattern on their stems made by the scars of former leaves. Some varieties rose in straight columns to a great height, sometimes more than a hundred feet, and then forked into a sudden canopy of leafy branches. The lower branches were tipped with drooping, cone-shaped clusters of fertile leaves, often bearing two kinds of spore. These were shed so profusely that in places they became piled like snow-drifts, forming an appreciable part of some seams of coal; and Seward pictures the great 'cones' swinging like censers as they cast their spores wastefully to the wind.

The calamites, although not so tall as the lepidodendrons, grew to about fifty feet. They were at their apogee in this age, and very diverse. All had a family resemblance to the humble horsetails, which are their only survivors now. They had regularly-jointed stems, slender for such tall trees, and bore

*Lester King, *The Morphology of the Earth*, 2nd edn., Oliver & Boyd 1967, p. 39.

their leaves in giant ruffs or whorls, clear-cut as a daisy-chain, in tapering tiers. There were smaller varieties in the undergrowth; and it is probably from one of them that the moderns are descended – from some sturdy dwarf that struggled on after the giants had died.

The lepidodendrons and the slim calamites would have seemed to us impressive and strange, but the family of ferns and seed-ferns were a festival of beauty. In an age of narrow leaves, they spread a lace-work of broad fronds. Some of them were small, like the ferns in an English wood; others were the first shade-giving trees; and a few lifted their green fountains above the calamites.

The seed-ferns are something of a mystery. Why did they become extinct? They were far ahead of all the other plants, and had found a full solution to the problem of reproduction on land. The flowering plants have improved on this, but have changed nothing essentially. We are consequently faced with an enigma. The seed-ferns discovered these principles first, and yet they became extinct; while the true ferns, which kept to the primitive method of alternating generations, still flourish. Seward has made this comment:

> Age after age there has been a repetition of unconscious effort towards the same end. Groups which had reached what might be regarded as an advanced state of efficiency became extinct; after a long interval, new creations repeated with little or no change in plan the structural design produced by long-forgotten and possibly blindly-ending lines of evolution. The pteridosperms [seed-ferns] of the later Palaeozoic floras, in the form of their leaves, in the construction of their seeds and male organs, as also in certain anatomical features, seem to foreshadow the flowering plants of the later ages. Is it possible that these analogies may be something more than instances of parallel development?*

His suggestion is that the seed-ferns may be ancestral to the flowering plants, although the line of descent is unknown, but this view is not generally accepted.

*A. C. Seward, *Plant Life through the Ages*, Cambridge University Press, 1931, p. 190.

THE GYMNOSPERMS

Every phase of evolution flows into the next, maintaining identity in difference; there is no enduring form and no frontier is absolute; it is necessary, however, to have a sense of period, because each has its character. For about fifty million years, the Palaeozoic forest was as we have pictured it; but it was not ubiquitous. There were also uplands, dry or even arid, where the trees thinned out and disappeared.

This borderland was a testing-ground for experiments in life. Its struggling inhabitants were not the norm of this age, but they would leave descendants well-suited to the next. An immense change was pending. The Earth was preparing for a great continental epoch – the greatest in the last thousand million years – and the conditions of life on the fringe of the forest most nearly resembled those that were to come. Before the end of the forest age, several plants had evolved a seed. These all produced two kinds of spore, one small and the other large. The small spores, which gave rise to the male cells, became a wind-born pollen; some of this was wafted to the large spores, in which the female cells were formed, and fertilization took place on the plant. Water for transportation had therefore become unnecessary, and the plants were free to conquer the Earth. Arrangements for intercepting the pollen varied; but all centred on an ovule, the large spore-bearing organ, which ripened into the seed. The ovules were carried on special leaves; and the great novelty that was being worked out in the dry borders of the forest was an elaboration of them by a new group of plants, the conifers.

In the conifers, then struggling to colonize unfriendly land, clusters of fertile leaves were grouped to form the scales of a cone. When the cone opened, drifting pollen was caught between the scales, and some of it found its way to the ovule at their base. Fertilization then took place and the seed began to form. In the flowering plants, the ovules are enclosed; but that further refinement still lay in the future, and these predecessors are known as plants with a naked seed – gymnosperms. Conifers are not the only gymnosperms; and it was the group as a whole that was destined, for a time, to possess the world.

In some, the pollen was already lightened for dispersal by an air-chamber, and in others, the seeds were already winged. These devices helped to ensure their triumph, and the air which had been their enemy became their servant.

REPTILES AND THERAPSIDS

A corresponding advance was being made at the same time and under the same austere conditions by some of the animals. The amphibians inhabited the humid forest; but on its borders, attempting to adapt themselves to a more arduous way of life, a small group was beginning to evolve the reptilian constitution. To some people the word reptile suggests a snake; but the snake is a late-comer – a highly specialized animal that has lost its legs. A typical reptile has legs, still short but lifting it higher than the amphibians, and feet with five toes in which every bone has a correspondence with our own hands and feet. The lizard is a fair example of reptilian design. And no one who has watched and been watched by a lizard can have failed to sense the lively mind that lies behind its darting movements. It was in a form rather like this that our ancestral stock became completely independent of the water.

As with the plants, the attainment of this new freedom required the solution of a reproductive problem. Amphibians approach one another in the breeding season, but eggs and sperm are still shed into the water and fertilization left to chance. It was the reptiles who invented the art of love. This was one of their two great achievements. It is scarcely conceivable that animals, like the plants, could come to rely on a wind-blown pollen for their propagation; and so internal fertilization was necessary to complete the colonization of the land. Some animal had to begin love-making, and it was the 'lizards'. One must add, however, the usual proviso that the arthropods had done it first. In fact the arthropods were almost an era in advance; and at a time when the vertebrates could scarcely waddle, they had already grown wings and giant dragonflies flitted among the Palaeozoic trees.

The second great achievement of the reptiles, also indispensable to full liberation from the water, was the land egg. It had to give to the developing embryo all that the water had once provided; it had to be the river, the lake, the sea in miniature; and to achieve this, the reptilian egg contains three sacs enclosed in membranes, the whole enveloped by another membrane covered with a parchment-like shell. One of the sacs is filled with a fluid by which the embryo is surrounded and protected, the second contains a supply of food, and the third receives waste products. A fourth membrane, the chorion, encloses them all.

With this kind of egg, the vertebrates could at last spend their whole lives on dry land. It was a fundamental advance. It began as a substitute for the ocean – or for the pond; but it was so much more efficient than either, and the embryo was so much better protected and nourished than it ever had been, that a great economy in egg-laying could be made. Female fishes shed millions of eggs into the sea, the human female releases one a month, and the reptilian egg is the link between these extremes.

The gymnosperms and the reptiles, therefore, belong together, and represent a comparable evolutionary stage in plants and animals. This completed the conquest of the land, but the naked seed and the naked egg were not the final answers to the reproductive problem. Life was waiting, as it were, for flowers and mammals. Neither of these appeared in the Palaeozoic Era, but there was a trend towards both. In the plants, this is displayed by the seed-ferns, and in the animals, by the mammal-like reptiles of Gondwanaland – the Therapsids.

It is not certain where the first reptiles appeared, but the early stages of the reptile-to-mammal transition are illustrated by a remarkable series in the South African rocks. These intermediate forms, the Therapsids, belong to the end of the Palaeozoic Era, and the trend to a mammalian constitution is thus shown to be very early; but a long period of stagnation followed this precocious beginning. The Mesozoic Era is rightly named the Age of Reptiles, and it was only near its close that true mammals became prominent. How is this early impetus and lengthy retardation to be explained? To do so, one must consider in what respects the reptiles were deficient, and what climatic conditions would expose this deficiency and set a premium upon change.

They had colonized both the super-continents by the Late

Palaeozoic; but the climate of Gondwanaland was very different from that of the tropical or sub-tropical north. When the Hercynian Mountains were rising and the northern forests were in decline, the Southern Ice Age had set in. The ice-sheets formed, retreated, and advanced again over large tracts of Australia, India, South Africa and South America.

One consequence of these contrasting climates was the division of the Earth into two distinct floral provinces. Before this time, the plants had been curiously similar in all parts of the world; but the chilling of the south resulted in a cold-adapted flora, which has no counterpart in the north, and which has been named after one of its most characteristic species of seed-fern, Glossopteris. The climatic severity that produced the Glossopteris flora may also have hastened, even if it did not primarily cause, the further evolution of the reptiles.

One failing of the reptiles was their inability to keep their bodies – and still less their eggs – at a constant temperature. When the weather was too hot or too cold, they became lethargic; and in extremes, they died. Those that had spread to Gondwanaland faced a very rigorous climate; and one has but to reflect on the fate of a naked egg in an ice age to recognize that, if animals were to survive under such conditions, the reptilian constitution would have to change.

The alterations necessary stand out as the most characteristic features of the mammals – the maintaining of a constant temperature, the retention of the egg in the maternal body until the young are ready to be born, and hair. All these are adaptations to the cold. It is therefore comprehensible that a tendency towards the mammalian constitution should have appeared during the Southern Ice Age. On the other hand, the climate in the north suited the reptiles very well; in fact it had partly created them; and they prospered in consequence throughout the coming era.

THE LAND BRAIN

Other changes were also necessary if animals were to live successfully on land – changes in their organs of perception, in their nerve-centres, and in their brains. From the outset, the brain has a gnostic function; and the Palaeozoic Era was not, like the eras of the Moon, psychically unrecorded. Minds as well as bodies emerged from the water, and they had to become adapted to deal with a new environment and to create a new world-picture.

From our own standpoint, looking back, the nervous organization of the amphibians and the reptiles is transitional. It is the ancient bequest that the mammals inherited and marvellously augmented. At this phase of its evolution there was still a triple brain – for smelling, seeing, and hearing – in which each part mediated its special sense; but in the forebrain, in the roof of the cerebral hemispheres, an area had begun to develop, which would finally integrate and dominate the whole.

In the primitive under-water forebrain, the walls of the hemispheres showed two special formations – the 'pear' on the outside and the 'sea-horse' on the inside walls. In the transitional brain, both of them were increased by the addition of layers of cells known as the 'old bark' of the forebrain – the palaeocortex overgrowing the 'pear', and the archicortex the 'sea-horse'. Between them lay the roof, which had so far been rudimentary. There now began a great development of this area; and as it expanded more rapidly than the rest, the simple, primitive pattern became deformed. The earlier formations were pressed downwards, and ultimately the 'old brain' was completely covered up. This enveloping region is termed the 'new bark' – the neocortex.

Nervous pathways were gradually established from the old centres further back to this new region; and where their fibre-tracts fanned out, terminated and discharged their information, counterparts of their centres of origin began to form in the neocortex. The result of this was that eventually the most important faculties and functions, previously dispersed, were drawn together into a single area where they became intimately connected with one another by a growing multitude of correlating cells. When the process was completed, in the mammals, this 'new brain' assumed lordship over all.

That something of the sort would happen might, perhaps, have been surmised from the beginning. Given the unifying function of the central nervous system, and some hundreds of millions of years for its elaboration, it might have been expected to evolve some predominant part; but not necessarily this particular part. Why was the forebrain thus favoured?

The question has intrigued many people, and there is no completely satisfying reply. The midbrain had a long lead and cannot have been incapable of further advance. But this did not happen.

In the amphibians most of the optic fibres still go to the midbrain; but there is an increase in the number deflected to the thalamus, and thence relayed forward. This is a continuing trend. In the reptiles the point of balance is reached and for the first time surpassed. Although the optic lobes continue to be important as reflex centres, they are being down-graded; and the seat of visual consciousness is being transferred to the hemispheres. This is also the case with the other senses. Only in the higher mammals is the transference complete; but it began with the amphibians, and reached a turning-point in the reptilian brain. This is perhaps its most interesting feature, and leads on to what has been described as 'the most successful experiment that nature ever made'.

Although the older brain-parts were being gradually subordinated to the new, their complexity also increased in the course of evolution. There was development at every level from the receptors upwards, and the expansion of the neocortex would have been impossible without a corresponding improvement in the nervous elements by which it is subserved. In a sense, it mirrors the lower centres, and its great significance is that it ultimately dominates and holostically comprehends them all. In ourselves, it is said to contain about fourteen thousand million nerve-cells, and it would seem to be by them that the tapestry of thought is woven; but this mind-weaving did not begin with us, and wherever the nervous threads exist, in however small a brain, there is experience of some fraction of the world's design.

THE GREAT CONTINENTAL EPOCH

'The majestic drift of super-continents through the climatic girdles of the Earth.' This sublime phrase might evoke a picture of a smooth and almost dream-like progress. At times, perhaps, it was so; but this is not the whole picture; and to complete it, one must recall the expression of another great geologist, who spoke of the periods of mountain building as

'Earth-storms'. There is an intimate connection between the 'drift' and the 'storm'.

We have seen an ice-age in the southern continent, a tropical forest in Europe, and the first woodlands flourishing in regions that are now a snow-bound, arctic waste. The transforming of these climates into ours implies a stupendous northward migration of the continental masses since the Palaeozoic Era. The trend was, perhaps, continuous; but it reached two periods of climax. These were the 'Earth-storms' that caused the Hercynian orogeny late in the Palaeozoic, and the Alpine orogeny in the Caenozoic Era. Both may be understood as due to the pressure of a northward-moving Gondwanaland (or Africa) of which the most spectacular consequence was the folding and uplifting of the younger, weaker rocks of the geosynclines between the continents – notably those of the Tethys.

Even at the beginning of the forest age, the sea-bed of the Tethys had been disturbed. Folds were then rising slowly into islands, but for millions of years the sultry peace of the vast green land was scarcely broken. There was volcanism occasionally: Arthur's Seat at Edinburgh was an active volcano during part of the period; there were other volcanoes in this region, and the lepidodendron forest that flourished to the north of them, covering what is now the Firth of Forth, was overwhelmed and in part preserved by an eruption of volcanic ash – a sylvan Pompeii more that three hundred million years old. But the forest age is not characterized by violence: the time between the mountains was, in the main, one of muted thunder and imprisoned fires.

The islands were none the less portents. They grew higher, more extensive, more perturbed. And gradually the former sea-bed was uplifted into the majestic ranges first of the Armorican and then of the Variscan Mountains. When one attempts to recreate these events in imagination, they seem almost like a *coup de théâtre*, like the rising of the magician's castle in Wagner's famous scene. Then, both to the west and to the east of this European stage, two other great chains arose on the present sites of the Appalachian and the Ural Mountains. It would seem that the crust of the Earth throughout the whole of this area was in a state of compression, and that ranges appeared where the yielding geosynclines were flanked by the forelands of old consolidated rocks. This period of mountain-building, which brought the Palaeozoic Era and its ancient forms of life to an end, is the Hercynian orogeny.

The Vosges, the Black Forest, the Böhmewald, and the Massif Centrale of France are among the vestiges of these vanished chains. The New Red Sandstone, which includes the red rocks of Devonshire, are a product of their erosion. The climate of this region was still hot, but it was becoming arid. Some of its rocks are composed of sediments deposited by watercourses flowing from the mountains; others are aeolean, laid down by scorching winds. But neither contains much evidence of life. The main outcome of this upsurge of the Earth was the creation of a vast new continent, the Hercynian Continent, which interrupted the Tethys for several million years. The hot, damp swamps, lagoons and lowlands were replaced by a landscape of mountains – beautiful, but severe. The forests perished, and the Great Continental Epoch began.

The birth of a continent is a terrible time for life. The changes are greater than any but the hardiest can bear. There had been a wave of extinctions when the Caledonian Mountains arose; but there had been no land-life then, and relatively speaking it was small. The extinctions that accompanied the Hercynian orogeny were on so vast a scale that they constitute a major division in biological time. They mark the turn of the eras. The devastation was greatest in marine life: a multitude of its most beautiful and elaborate forms was swept away, leaving only the simple and unspecialized to initiate new lines in the ensuing age. The amphibians suffered almost as much, and for them there was no recovery; their way of life continued in places, but it was ended for ever as the dominant form. Only plants with a seed, and animals that could mate and lay their eggs on land were able to thrive in this altered world. The most advanced of these were the gymnosperms and the reptiles. Hitherto, they had been a struggling minority, but the coming age was theirs; and so the ancient gave place to the intermediate forms of life, and the Palaeozoic to the Mesozoic Era.

CHAPTER FIVE

The Mesozoic World

THE TREND OF CHANGE

The Mesozoic Era began about 225,000,000 B.P. It was much shorter than the preceding era; but even so, it lasted over a hundred and fifty million years; and it is as well to remind ourselves that to sum up the history of such vast spans of time, whether in a single chapter or in many volumes, is always to oversimplify. The details are beyond the grasp of the human mind. In popular imagination, this is the era of the dinosaurs; and although they appeared only in the latter part of it, they deserve this distinction. They were its unique extravagance. But this was also the time when the flowering plants, the birds and the mammals – almost the whole living fabric of our familiar world – made their tentative beginning.

The general character of the Mesozoic is exhibited in bold simplicity by the English south coast. The red cliffs and the white are monuments to its trend of change. The red cliffs of Devonshire – the New Red Sandstone – belong to the Great Continental Epoch with which the era began. The white cliffs of Dover, made up of tiny shells, were laid down beneath the sea, and they mark its close. Between them, in parts of Wiltshire, there are remains of coral reefs. This revealing sequence – from the deserts to the corals, and from the corals to the white shells – shows that the world was undergoing a great sea-change.

We have pictured the Palaeozoic largely in terms of two orogenies, and of the period of forests that lies between. But the Mesozoic may be best imagined as the time when the seas came back. When the era opened, the Tethys, although not obliterated, was land-locked. If one stands today on the Devonshire cliffs and looks out to sea, one may imagine that in the early part of the Mesozoic, rather more than two hundred million years ago, there was no sea, and that the Sahara-like country of deserts and oases, to which the red sandstone rocks bear witness, extended uninterrupted across the Channel and the Bay of Biscay, over France, Spain, and the Western Mediterranean to Africa. There was, however, no Italy. The coast of the Tethys then edged Sardinia and Corsica, and ran northwards following more or less the present line of the Alps. Although hilly in places, it was not then a mountainous coast; but it represented a foreland, or region of resistance, along which mountains would be piled up when the Alpine movements came. It is known as the Vindelician threshold.

When the old Hercynian Continent reached a state of decrepitude, its once-splendid mountains worn away, it became an arid land of low relief, and an easy conquest for the returning sea. It required only a moderate subsidance, which often follows a period of uplift, to cause an inundation. This partly explains why the era is one of extremes; and why the great continental epoch, with which it began, slowly changed into a great marine epoch.

The first invasion came from the east. The sea that covered the region that is now the Himalayas spread slowly across Persia and reunited with the shrunken Tethys. The expansion continued to the north-west, and the Vindelician threshold became a festoon of islands. Beyond this spread a Germanic sea. Its waters were not deep; and the massifs, which were the remains of the old degraded mountains, formed an archipelago in which the shape and extent of the islands varied with crustal movements, being linked, parted, re-shaped and linked again.

The ice-caps of the southern glaciation were then melting, and this added to the volume of the seas. Reaching an arm northward, the Tethys joined the Arctic Ocean; another arm stretched westward, submerging Spain; then came the inundation of the Russian platform; and, so far as Europe was concerned, nothing remained of the old Hercynian continent but an archipelago. Giant reptiles splashed and floundered in its shallow waters. Coral islands rose in France, in Germany, in Wiltshire. The climate of this region was sub-tropical, not unlike that of the Great Barrier Reef today; but it was tending to become temperate, and the Great Chalk Sea, with which the era ended, was distinctly cooler than the coral seas.

About 100,000,000 B.P. the marine expansion reached its maximum. Most of the Sahara was then submerged, and a vast seaway spread across Western America. This was a world-climax and the waters then slowly withdrew. If one makes due allowance for the immensities of time and change, one may picture the Mesozoic world as a central archipelago flanked by three areas – North America, Gondwanaland, and Northern

Asia – which remained predominantly land. Continental forms of life continued in these regions to thrive and to progress.

THE TRIUMPH OF THE GYMNOSPERMS

The great forest trees of this time, replacing and often excelling the lepidodendrons that had vanished, were the conifers. They were of many varieties; no species then living has survived; but some of them foreshadowed modern trees, and gave promise, as it were, of the cypresses and the giant redwoods. In the Mesozoic Era, when vegetation once more became remarkably uniform throughout the world, they flourished everywhere; and in favoured places there were forests of unexcelled magnificence. The petrified forest of Arizona is a vestige of one of these. The remains of trees over two hundred feet high have been found there; and some of their huge trunks, by petrifaction of the strangest sort, have been changed into jasper, agate, and chalcedony.

The cycads have also a conspicuous place in any picture of the Mesozoic landscape. A small company of cycads, mostly tropical, is still living. They are of no importance in the modern flora, but their ancestors were a mighty race. They were not palm-trees, but they looked rather like palms; and in the days of their prosperity they were equally diverse. Some had curiously swelling stems, like the columns of an Egyptian temple; others rose straight as a date-palm to culminate in a similar crown of fronds. They had faced the deserts of the continental age, and were able to withstand drought and intense sunlight. In contrast to the grace of the fern-trees, their foliage had a stiff and stylized look; and this was accentuated in some varieties by a remarkable experiment in 'flowers'. The modified leaves which composed these curious organs seem like a compromise between the scales of a cone and the petals of a flower, but the ovules were never enclosed. In rocks that are at present exposed along the Yorkshire coast, where once a Mesozoic jungle spread, so many of these cycad 'flowers' have been preserved that they are locally known as 'cliff-roses'.

Except for the many fern-like plants, only one other Mesozoic group is outstanding – the ginkgos. They were splendid billowing trees, widely-distributed and of many genera. Fan-shaped leaves resembling those of a ginkgo have been found in Palaeozoic rocks, and although it cannot be proved that they belonged to forbears of this line, it is a reasonable supposition. If this is correct, then the one surviving species of ginkgo is the doyen of all living trees. This is the sacred maidenhair tree which no longer grows in a wild state but has been reverentially preserved in temple gardens in the Far East – one of man's few acts of piety towards nature to set against his vast despoliation.

These three groups, and some ferns, dominate the Mesozoic flora and give it a distinctive character. It must, however, be supposed, despite our ignorance, that the flowering plants, which seem to burst suddenly on the world near the close of the era, had somewhere made an unobtrusive beginning.

THE MAMMALIAN DESIGN

By the middle of the era, when Europe was a maze of tropical islands, the dinosaurs had spread everywhere and their lordship was undisputed. In the tangled thickets beneath the cycads and the fern-trees, however, there was a small but important population of another kind. They were timid, inquisitive creatures, already subdividing into species, and most of them were no larger than a good-sized mouse. These were the early mammals. They posed no threat to the ruling reptiles. They were performing a series of delicate experiments on themselves. In the shade of the Mesozoic woodlands, they were quietly persistent in this for many millions of years; and by the end of the era, they had evolved a new pattern of life.

Their history prior to this age cannot be traced with certainty. Even among the early reptiles, there were some groups that showed a tendency to develop a mammalian character. We have noticed this in the Therapsids of Gondwanaland. This was only a trend, the Therapsids were not true mammals; but it must have been during the Great Continental Epoch that a line leading to the true mammals parted company from the main reptilian stock. It is possible that this happened in South Africa, where the rocks of the Karroo contain a remarkable collection of transitional forms. These may, like the seed-ferns, have been blindly-ending lines; but they show a considerable number of species, and it has been remarked of one of them, Cynognathus: 'Were he alive, he probably would seem to us an odd cross between a lizard and a dog, a transitional type between two great groups of back-boned animals.'* This was the state of affairs when the era began.

Living conditions during the Mesozoic, particularly the warm equable climate, greatly favoured the reptiles and they became dominant, freely developing a phantasy of form that sometimes seems more appropriate to the realms of mythology. Presumably, the mammalian trend was consequently checked, but it was not extinguished. The larger types disappeared, but among small animals progress continued. The first authentic mammals known to us belong to the middle of the Mesozoic and are only a little later than the dinosaurs. The existing animals they most resemble are some of the small marsupials of Australasia, but they were not quite like anything that is now alive. These were our Mesozoic ancestors – probably arboreal and possibly nocturnal. They were improving themselves and quietly biding their time.

The mammals are so-named because they provide their young with milk, but this is only one of their unique character-istics: they have also special teeth, better brains, and hair in place of scales or feathers. And they have made yet another fundamental advance – which the birds achieved independently – that of maintaining their bodies at a constant temperature. This freed them to a great extent from dependence on climate, and permitted activity in both summer and winter, either by day or by night. The reptiles, as has been noticed, were at a great disadvantage in this respect.

The mammalian design should be thought of as a whole. Every element in it is important, and each, by reciprocal influence, stimulated the development of the rest; but if one wishes to lay stress on a particular feature, then it must be the decisive shift of the highest nervous centres to the roof of the forebrain with the consequent evolution of the neocor-tex.

The neocortex is composed of six layers of cells, but its structural principles are derived from the earlier triple lamina-tion. In the old midbrain, it will be recalled, there were three

*A. S. Romer, *Man and the Vertebrates*, Penguin Books 1954, p. 126.

layers in the roof of the optic lobes. The first, at the top, consisted of the incoming fibres of the optic tract; their information was received by a second layer of small correlating cells; and impulses from these went to a third layer of large motor cells, with long axons, which controlled the muscular responses. The neocortex is an elaboration of this arrangement. In the course of its embryological development it may be seen that the original layer of correlating cells divides into three, and the original bottom layer into two. In the human foetus, this begins to happen at about six months, and regional distinctions follow.

When the old correlating layer subdivides, many large cells with relatively long branches develop in it; but they do not discharge into motor centres. The activity of these cells is confined to brain-events, their function is inter-cortical association, and their impulses do not necessarily result in any show of outward behaviour. What does this mean? Surely, that this new structure is concerned with the fuller extraction of meaning from experience, with increasing intelligence, and with the capacity for thought.

In so far as mind may be said to have a location, it is here that those mental events take place that we ourselves experience, and that are inferable, in a simpler form, in our mammalian relations. One must suppose that every organism has as much mind or psyche as its nervous structure can express; and that by observing the development of the structure, we may infer the evolution of the mind.

The psychological consequences of the invasion of the hemispheres were momentous, and led on to our own mental pattern. As we have already noticed, it was inevitable from the beginning that mind should evolve as a small surface of consciousness on a relatively vast unconscious. This is the precondition of Freud's analysis into ego, id and super-ego. After describing these functions, Freud went on to say:

This general schematic picture of a psychical apparatus may be supposed to apply as well to the higher animals which resemble man mentally. A super-ego must be presumed to be present wherever, as in the case of man, there is a long period of dependence in childhood. A distinction between ego and id is an unavoidable assumption.

Animal psychology has not yet taken in hand the interesting problem which is here presented.*

Our achievements and our tragedies do not begin with Oedipus and Electra, nor with primitive man, nor even with the primates: they are rooted in the mammalian constitution itself, and in the ways of living and thinking that it has imposed. The psyche as such is, of course, much older. It is as old as the living bodies the responses of which its first function is to guide; it has evolved with them; and the whole course of biological evolution would need to be taken into account for a full understanding of its phenomenology.

THE FIRST BIRDS

The mammals were not the only forerunners of the coming age to inhabit these Mesozoic islands. There were also the first birds, but very little is known of them. Our ignorance of the history of the birds serves as a reminder of the unbalance of the fossil-record. Marine animals with shells are the most likely, and aerial creatures with slender bones among the least likely, to be preserved as fossils. We have such a detailed knowledge of the ammonites of this time that a rock can be dated with confidence by the species it has preserved; but the remains of only two birds of the Middle Mesozoic have as yet been discovered – a mere intimation of their existence. Then follows a gap of millions of years.

The first known birds, Archaeopteryx, lived among the coral islands of southern Germany. The two that were fossilized perished on the mud-flats where they doubtless came to feed; and this mud has turned into the lithographic stone of Solnhofen, which has yielded a remarkable collection of fossils. The remains of more than five hundred animal species have been found in it, including many types of flying-lizard, millions of crinoids, and a dinosaur. It was evidently a feeding-ground exposed at low tide. The immediate shore consisted of reefs and atolls, which fringed the coast of a large island occupying the region that is now the Bavarian Alps. In the Mesozoic, this

*Sigmund Freud, *An Outline of Psycho-Analysis,* revised edn., edited by James Strachey, Hogarth Press 1969, p. 4.

island was a jungle of fern-trees, cycads, and cypress-like conifers; and it was the home of the first birds.

Archaeopteryx was about the size of a crow – very insignificant compared with the giant flying-reptiles some of which had a wing-span of more than twenty feet. The birds, like the mammals, had evolved from reptilian stock, and they still retained many of its features. These still had teeth, a lizard-like tail, and three usable fingers on each wing. Nevertheless, they were true birds; and although it is doubtful if they were warm-blooded, it is certain that they had feathers. Although they are not known in any other locality, it is probable that they were fairly widespread; because the next fossil birds yet discovered, belonging to the end of the era, were found in North America. In the Middle Mesozoic, however, the birds and the mammals were no more than a hint of the future. The dinosaurs were then lords of the present, and they had adapted themselves to every region of the Earth.

GIANTISM AND PHANTASY

The Mesozoic is in many ways an era for the connoisseur. Its most spectacular creations – the dinosaurs, the flying-lizards, and the ammonites – left no descendants; they might have lived and died on another planet for all the influence they have had on present life; but in the course of a hundred million years or so, they reached the limits of the possible in giantism and grotesquerie. 'Believe it or not,' their remains would seem to whisper, 'life *can* be like this!' And having proved it, exhausted one might think by such a preposterous demonstration, they became extinct. Not one dinosaurian gene has been transmitted to the modern world: all present-day reptiles, a mere remnant of the Mesozoic host, are descended from much humbler stock.

The dinosaurs have been so well-served by palaeontologists, writers and artists that they are almost as familiar as our contemporary fauna; and they are permanently established in man's imagination as *the* prehistoric animal. They were not, however, in the mainstream of evolution, and so we shall not dwell on them here; but this is not to belittle their importance or their fascination. On the whole, they could be considered

Man developed his brain & hands and learned to speak.

Ape-man: a mammal who stood upright & used his hands for making weapons & tools.

Other mammals developed larger brains & sharper senses: and continued to evolve.

Some mammals developed huge bodies heavily armed with tusks & horns: but their brains remained small & they died out.

The placental mammals kept their young inside their bodies until they were almost ready to look after themselves.

Eggs were broken & stolen by other animals. The marsupial mammals gave birth to undeveloped young & kept them safely in pouches.

The early mammals were small. They laid eggs like reptiles, but instead of scales they had a warm covering of fur.

Mammals evolved from reptiles, probably from the simple strong-legged theromorphs.

The Evolution of the Mammals (*Messrs* **P. R.** *Gawthorn Ltd*)

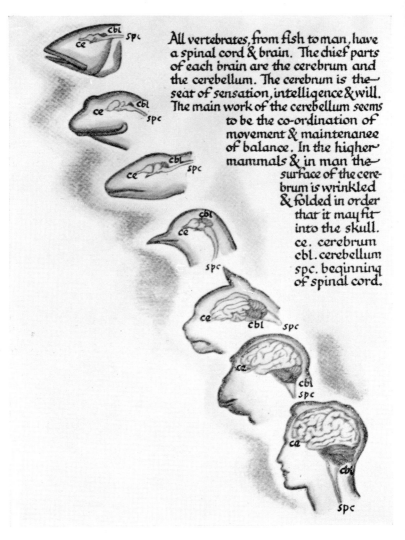

All vertebrates, from fish to man, have a spinal cord & brain. The chief parts of each brain are the cerebrum and the cerebellum. The cerebrum is the seat of sensation, intelligence & will. The main work of the cerebellum seems to be the co-ordination of movement & maintenance of balance. In the higher mammals & in man the surface of the cerebrum is wrinkled & folded in order that it may fit into the skull.
ce. cerebrum
cbl. cerebellum
spc. beginning of spinal cord.

The Evolution of the Brain *(Messrs P. R. Gawthorn Ltd)*

fortunate. Some writers have described them as a failure, but all forms must perish at last. Their race had a very long lifespan, they enjoyed a kindly climate, and they inhabited what must have been a beautiful world. They may not have appreciated beauty, but every creature that is in harmony with its surroundings finds pleasure in them, and every life seems precious to itself.

The Mesozoic is characteristically a marine epoch, and so most of its organic remains are those of creatures that lived in the sea. Here, also, phantasy and giantism prevailed. There were crinoids with stems fifty feet long, and the coiled shells of the ammonites ranged from a few tenths of an inch to nine feet in diameter. These are the largest shells that have ever been found, and they are often richly ornamented. The inhabitants of this under-sea world seem to have had a passion for self-adornment and a taste for travel. We shall not now enter their special domain; but the ammonites demand notice, because they are the guide-fossil of the era. The correlation of its rocks depends mainly on their changing species, it is due to them that the geological order is better understood in the Mesozoic than in any other era; and they also afford an exemplary study in evolution, because of the long and detailed record of their transformations.

They first appeared in the Middle Palaeozoic, and about two hundred genera of that era are known. The wave of extinction that accompanied the Hercynian orogeny destroyed them all except one simple generalized group. In the Early Mesozoic, a great resurgence took place from these survivors; and in the course of some forty million years, this single stock gave rise to more than four hundred genera. Then a new calamity befell the race, for reasons that are less easily explained, and nearly all these diverse forms were swept away. They were again reduced to one or a few simple species; but conditions in the middle of the era suited them, and they began to diversify once more. Twelve hundred genera have so far been discovered in this period; but at the end of the era, the ultimate disaster overtook them, and they became extinct.

THE FLOWERING OF THE NORTH

In the second half of the Mesozoic Era, the plants made their most spectacular advance since the first land-flora raised firm stems towards the sun. In the age before the spreading of the Great Chalk Sea, rather more than a hundred million years ago, flowering plants are known to have existed. These are the earliest records; but they are of well-developed forms, which must have had a long ancestry that is still unknown. There is no hint of it in the south. And it is in Greenland, at a time when a characteristic Mesozoic flora covered the rest of the known world, that we find, as Seward puts it, 'the first steps of a steeply-ascending stairway leading to the plant-world as we know it today'.

The rocks that have yielded these surprising remains are on Disko Island. This is now seven hundred miles north of the Arctic Circle, off the Greenland coast of the Baffin Sea. Across the sea to the north-west is Ellesmere Land, which had been the home of the first woodlands some two hundred million years before. This sea is now bestrewn with icebergs; but in Mesozoic times, it was a forested plain. This was the land of the first flowers. At present, Disko Island has a meagre arctic flora, with prostrate willows and dwarf birch, bearing eloquent witness to the rigours of the polar climate; but then

> there were forests of conifers and flowering trees and an abundance of ferns belonging to families that are now mainly tropical; it was a vegetation which in size of leaf, as in the breadth of the rings of growth seen in petrified logs of wood, gives no sign of a physical environment such as we now find on the edge of an arctic land most of which now lies under a storm-lashed mantle of ice.*

The reconstruction of this flora affords a fascinating picture. Out of a world of almost-mythical remoteness, our familiar world is taking shape. At this place and time, the two were curiously blended. The ginkgos still waved their evergreen

*A. C. Seward, *Plant Life through the Ages*, Cambridge University Press, 1931, p. 393.

fans, there were conifers of species that have vanished, and cycads brandished their swordlike fronds; but mingled with them, and more numerous, were the homely plane-tree, the magnolia, the oak, and some others, no less modern but now tropical, such as the cinnamon and the bread-fruit tree. These new-comers are all flowering plants; this is the first indisputable evidence of their existence; and if the secret of their origin lies somewhere in these frozen wastes, it will be difficult to uncover.

These new plants had made progress in a number of ways, but especially in their manner of reproduction. Most flowers, but not all, are bisexual – that is to say, the pollen and the ovules are produced in the same blossom. They may, therefore, be self-fertilizing; but usually they are not, and the pollen of one flower is in some way transported to the ovules of another. We have noticed some of the experiments that led up to this. In the conifers, the ovules lie naked at the base of the cone-scales and the pollen is drifted to them by the wind. The cycad 'flowers' were more advanced. They were sometimes bisexual, and although the ovules were still naked, there were the beginnings of a protective device. True flowers have developed this, and the ovules are safely enclosed: this containing vessel is the ovary that ripens into the fruit. The ovary itself is derived from the spore-bearing leaf, and so the evolutionary sequence is made plain – from the little fertile leaves of the Old Red Sandstone flora, to the cherry and the pear. All plants that have an ovary, and consequently bear a fruit, are known as plants with an enclosed seed – angiosperms. And this marks the present summit of floral evolution.

Some flowering plants depend on the wind for pollination. In them the sexes are separate, and they often bear drooping catkins, from which the pollen is easily shaken by the breeze. As the wind needs no inducement, they are devoid of ornament, and their flowers are easily overlooked. They have no petals, no nectar, no perfume. All these are the blandishments of plants that rely on insects. The desired visitor is offered nectar, and guided to it by colour and scent. While feeding, a little pollen is dusted on to its body, and this is carried to the scene of the next meal, where some will be brushed off and may fertilize a neighbouring flower. It is the most delightful partnership in nature, and it was not by chance that the spread of the flowering plants coincided with a great enrichment of the insect world.

Before the end of the era, attractiveness had come to have survival value; a beauty-contest had begun among the flowers; there were already some familiar shapes, scents and colours, and the hum of the bees.

This flora spread southward in successive waves. The commingling of temperate and tropical genera is characteristic of it; but in the ensuing era, when climates became more exacting again and much more diverse, it was sorted out, as it were, into its present zones. Botanically speaking, this invasion of the world by the angiosperms is the most important event in the Mesozoic Era; but it happened towards the end, and their great unfolding belongs to the next era. Like the mammals and the birds, flowers are not typical of the Mesozoic, but a foretaste of the future, and this intermediate period rightly belongs to the gymnosperms. The petrified forest, the 'cliff-roses', the maidenhair tree in the temple garden – these are the relics of the characteristic Mesozoic flora. These venerable plants possessed the Earth for a hundred million years, but they were conquered at last by a flower.

'FOR WHOM THE BELL TOLLS'

Forms are, so to speak, provisional; and the enhancement of life requires their eventual supersession. If they were not superseded, life would be imprisoned; its freedom is inseparable from change; and the discovery of evolution, by displaying the process, has released us from the concept of an endless incarceration in some particular shape. It will not be a matter for regret, if life has then found some better vehicle of expression, when the human form becomes extinct. And as it was with the dinosaurs, so it will be with us.

Extinction came to the dinosaurs at the end of the Mesozoic Era. But what was the reason? There is still no satisfying answer. It has been suggested, in desperation one might suppose, that it was due to the rise of the Rocky Mountains! It is likely that the dinosaurs who lived in that part of the world did dislike the Rocky Mountains, or the disturbances that preceded their uplift; but these were local phenomena, and the dinosaurs had spread over the Earth. Some of their best skeletons have been discovered in South Africa, the Gobi

Desert has yielded their finest eggs, and they have left their footprints in Dorsetshire. Some species, moreover, had taken to the sea. But they all became extinct, rather abruptly as such happenings go, at the end of the Mesozoic.

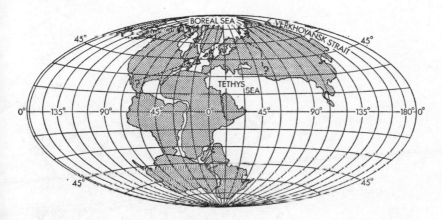

a. Reconstruction of continents in mid-Mesozoic time assuming that continental drift occurred due to spreading from mid-ocean ridges along paths now marked by aseismic ocean ridges. The dashed lines represent some earlier mountains formed by unions of old continental blocks (*Nature* and Professor J. Tuzo Wilson)

It is possible that they were carried off by an epidemic, but rheumatoid arthritis is the only complaint that some of them are known to have had. This was no doubt painful in so large a frame, but it does not account for their disappearance. A change in vegetation, the coming of a modern flora, might have left them short of food. But there is still something mysterious in the way they vanished. One thing, at least, is certain: they were not forcibly dispossessed by the small, timid, but intelligent mammals who were to inherit the Earth.

Geographically and climatically, the world of the mammals was to be vastly different from that of the two super-continents we have so far envisaged; and the break-up of these ancient lands is the dramatic climax of this era. Gondwanaland disintegrated first; and before the end of the Mesozoic, it had been completely dismembered. There have been many transforma-

b. Fit of all the continents around the Atlantic at the 500 fm. contour, transverse Mercator projection (The Royal Society and Sir Edward Bullard, F.R.S.)

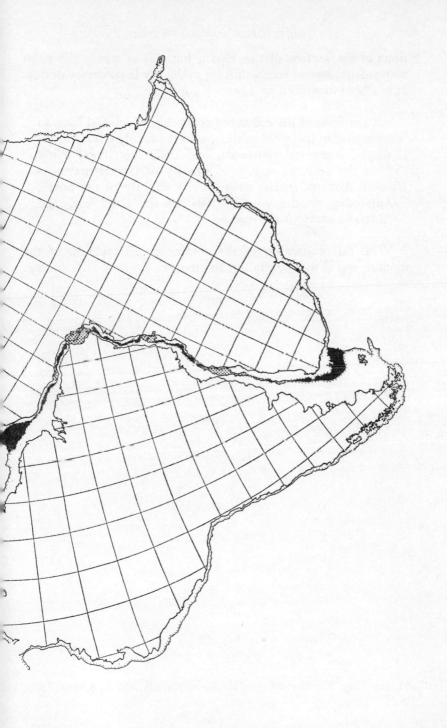

tions of the surface of the Earth, but this is surely the most stupendous piece of scene-shifting in the whole planetary drama. It has been described by Lester King as

> . . . partition of the old super-continent, which had been so satisfying in its ovoid outline, into the family of curiously-shaped southern continents, and their centrifugal flight from the original centre of gravity of Gondwanaland – South America to the west, Africa slightly to the north, Antarctica to the south, India to the northeast, and Australia away to the east.*

With this scattering of the continents, the pattern of the modern world was beginning to emerge.

*Lester King, *The Morphology of the Earth,* 2nd edn., Oliver & Boyd 1967, p. 62.

CHAPTER SIX

The Caenozoic World

THE NORTH ATLANTIC

The Caenozoic Era covers the last seventy million years. Geologically speaking, it is characterized by three spectacular events: first, the opening of the North Atlantic Ocean; then the Alpine orogeny – a term which includes the building of the entire Alpine-Himalayan mountain-system; and finally the Great Ice Age.

It was near the middle of the era, about thirty-five million years ago, that the first violent phase of the Alpine movements began. The main orogenic disturbance continued intermittently for at least fifteen million years. It was succeeded by a period of relative tranquillity – an age of lakes and forests in Europe and of spreading grasslands in Asia, throughout which the climate was steadily cooling. This culminated in a final uplift of the mountains, and then in the inexplicable disaster – quite recent from the geological point of view and from which we may not have fully emerged – the Great Ice Age. In Europe and Asia, the era may be imagined broadly in four periods: the Pre-Alpine, covering the first half of it, which was hot in Europe, volcanically disturbed in some regions, but mainly peaceful; the age of the major Alpine movements, which was still warm, but restless throughout and occasionally very violent; a period of Post-Alpine calm, a time of lakes, forests, steppes, and a climate that was steadily freshening; and then the ice.

In the region that had once formed the European Archipelago, the characteristic activity at the turn of the eras was slow uplift. This had its fluctuations, and in the Early Caenozoic there were occasional transgressions of the sea; but the general picture is the gradual enlargement of the European islands, until little by little they coalesced. Once again, the greater part of Europe became land, and the Mesozoic geography was reversed: where there had been a sea dotted with islands, there came to be a low-lying country dotted with lakes, marshes and land-locked basins. On the present site of the Alps and the Carpathians, there was still a geosynclinal sea; and the Tethys spread uninterrupted to the Far East.

This may give the impression of a fairly tranquil age; but this was also the time when the northern super-continent was breaking up, and one region was being transformed in a spectacular manner. Until the latter part of the Mesozoic, there seems to have been only one true ocean, so that both the eastern and the western ends of the Tethys reached it. But by the Early Caenozoic, the South Atlantic and Indian Oceans were already in existence, and the North Atlantic was taking shape.

The creation of the North Atlantic has sometimes been envisaged as the sinking of a vast land-mass – the submergence of an 'Atlantis' millions of years earlier than the catastrophe of which Plato dreamed. But it is now known that the ocean-floor shows no trace of a continental mass that has foundered, and the Atlantic must therefore be due to the gradual widening of a rift. At the opening of the Caenozoic, the Earth's crust was apparently in a state of tension in this area, and one outcome was volcanism on a scale for which there are few if any parallels. In places that now lie far apart – Ireland, Scotland, the Faroe Islands, Iceland and Greenland – there is evidence of a tremendous outpouring of basaltic lavas through fissures and volcanoes. And if one may look on this as the birth-throes of the North Atlantic, then the Giants' Causeway is perhaps the best-known monument to the event.

This rift, which opened in the latter part of the Mesozoic Era,* has been growing wider ever since. The rate has varied; and at the present time, it is thought to be about one centimetre a year. Recent discoveries in marine geology have shown that the Mid-Atlantic Ridge marks the line of separation, and that the ocean-floor is spreading on both sides of it. This ridge is a range of submarine mountains, but they differ from continental mountains in being composed entirely of igneous rock. It is also an earthquake belt, and coincides with a gigantic crack through which new material welling up from the interior of the Earth is being continually added to the crust. This accretion, when it solidifies, causes the ocean floors to grow from the mid-line; and they appear to behave like rigid plates, pushing the continents apart. The theory of 'plate tectonics' would explain the history of the oceans, and has important implications for that

*In *The Advancement of Science,* March 1971, a paper by A. T. S. Ramsay gives the following estimates in years B.P. for the opening of the Atlantic rifts: separation of South Africa and South America 138 million, of Europe and North America 93 million, and of North Europe and Greenland 65 million.

of the continents. Indeed, Sir Edward Bullard considers that geology is now a rejuvenating science, poised to make a spectacular advance.

THE PLACENTAL MAMMALS

The severance of land-connections in the North Atlantic had one important compensation: activity in the western geosyncline of North America resulted in a land-link across the Bering Straits. America had lost touch with Europe, but it gained access to Asia. The Bering Isthmus then enjoyed a temperate climate; and although it was interrupted occasionally, it must henceforth be pictured as one of the great pathways of animal migration.

On the Asiatic side of this isthmus was a continent then enjoying a period of exceptional stability; and it was here that some of the most important, curious and even grotesque developments in mammalian evolution took place. At the time, this land-mass was separated from Europe by a long, shallow sea which joined the Tethys in the region that is now Turkestan. There were no Himalayas as yet, and India was still an island not long severed from Gondwanaland. The southern coast of Asia ran through Tibet, and then turned south to include Malaysia. These shores, like the European end of the Tethys, had a tropical vegetation; but the vast hinterland, right to the coast of the Arctic Ocean, had in general the character of a temperate forest. By the Early Caenozoic, much of its flora was modern or nearly so – beech, walnut, birch and hazel. According to present evidence, it was here that the placental mammals evolved.

It is clear that the finding of important fossils is largely a matter of luck. New discoveries may at any time require a change in our provisional notions of the place of origin of any particular group and of the paths of its distribution. But the main course of the evolutionary sequence is a different question. There is no doubt that the stages of our own descent are placentals, primates, anthropoids; but the localities in which these strides were first taken are still partly problematical; and in this field, we can but consider what is likely and remain open-minded towards possible revision. The record of the placentals, as we now have it, begins in Central Asia, near the end of the Mesozoic; and this region accordingly assumes a unique interest. The first placentals were the contemporaries of the last dinosaurs. They were also the most advanced form of mammalian life: the new era was pre-eminently theirs.

It is because mammals are the most complicated of all animals that they are also the slowest to reach maturity. And the fact of taking so long to grow up gives them the chance to become more complicated. If complexity is a good thing, therefore, they have set up a virtuous circle. The obvious requirement of this kind of progress – and the simplest measure of it – is a lengthening period of parental care, and this results in a new web of family relationships which develops into the texture of society. Maturity is reached in two stages – pre-natal and post-natal; and the great mammalian experiment, of which we are one outcome, involved changes in both. The earliest mammals laid eggs, and the duck-billed platypus still does. The others acquired some means of retaining the egg in the warmth and security of the maternal body until the embryo was ready to emerge.

One of the main achievements of the reptiles, it will be recalled, was the evolution of the land-egg. In the advance made by the placental mammals, the parchment-like shell of the reptilian egg is lost, but all its other structures remain, and each is gradually adapted to a new use. The outermost membrane of the reptilian egg was the chorion; it is from a part of the chorion, in close contact with the lining of the womb, that the placenta develops. Various forms of this new organ were evolved, some more efficient than others, but all of them subserve the same end: they ensure that the vital needs of the embryo – respiration, nutrition, excretion – shall be supplied through exchanges with its mother's body. The outcome is the prolongation of pre-natal life which is characteristic of the placentals.

The vast majority of contemporary mammals are placentals; but those that lay eggs, the monotremes, and those that keep their young in pouches, the marsupials, evolved before them, and they still survive. They are only relatively unsuccessful; but the longer period of pre-natal life gave the placentals an advantage, because it was the first requirement of a more complicated adult form. The second requirement was a longer span of childhood, demanding a steady increase in parental care, and from this sprang a unique set of relationships. It is evident that these relationships, when they were further developed in the group, have led to vices as well as virtues; but it is fair to emphasize the virtues. In a mammalian family, the parents must love and teach; the young must respect and learn; and dispositions appropriate to these needs are woven into the fabric of a mammalian community. There is nothing mysterious, therefore, in the evolution of what we call the virtues. The higher forms of life could not have come into existence without them; and it would require only one generation of purely selfish parents for all the mammals – and most of the birds – to become extinct.

The remains of the earliest placentals known to us come from what is now the Gobi Desert, and belong to the end of the Mesozoic Era. This region was then a temperate forest, and these were small animals who lived in the trees. Their diet was probably mixed and consisted partly of insects. A fair representative of this group is Deltatheridium. Its skull was only about two inches long, and it bore some resemblance to a modern tree-shrew. This little arboreal creature, or one very like it, was the common ancestor of all the placentals.

The placental design met with rapid success. The primitive mammals, monotremes and marsupials, were soon ousted from the centre of the stage and relegated to the immense chorus of the dispossessed. By the turn of the eras, the new actors had stolen all the star parts and had spread to Europe and America. They were then diversifying rapidly, and it was at about this time that some of them took to the ground. As all the placentals had originally been arboreal, this event marks a great parting of the ways.

Those that became ground-dwellers found it an advantage to be swift of foot, and in consequence their front limbs became more and more specialized as legs; but those that remained arboreal needed a firm, precise grasp, a keen eye as they moved among the branches, and an appropriate co-ordination in the brain. Our own ancestors continued to live in the trees; and from this point onwards, it is probable that the most important single factor conducing to the eventual evolution of the human brain was the co-ordination of hand and eye. There was accordingly a great cleavage in the mammalian family at this time: its members had to choose, as it were, between swiftness and dexterity. The one resulted in the perfecting of foot and nose, the other, of hand and eye; and this entailed the preferential development of different areas in the brain.

In the strict sense of cousinship – descent from a common ancestor – the dog and the horse are as much man's cousins as are the anthropoids. The difference is merely of time and of appearance – of when the common ancestor lived. The ancestor we share with the dog was one of the early placentals living near the beginning of the Caenozoic Era, the one we have in common with the anthropoids was a fairly advanced primate living near the middle of the era, and with our first cousins we share descent from the old gentleman in the silver frame on the mantelpiece. But it is all one family. Its ties are no figure of speech. And as evolutionary time-spans go, this particular group is comparatively recent. It is not until we have sensed this kinship deeply, which is more than merely knowing it, that we can fully understand ourselves and appreciate our true position in the world.

AN AGE OF PLENTY

During the first period of their radiation, following the extinction of the dinosaurs, the mammals were exceptionally lucky. They did not have to conquer the Earth. It was left to them. And most of it at that time was luxuriant. Every aspect of nature was being transformed: the plants had begun to blossom and to shed and renew their leaves, some of the insects had become butterflies, and some of the reptiles had changed into birds. The climate was not rigorous anywhere; and although some regions were disturbed by continental movements, the mammals spread everywhere and colonized the Earth.

As the world then offered a fairly easy way of life, there was no great premium on brains. The mammals were intrinsically more intelligent than any other animal, and they were not yet in strenuous competition with one another. After the Alpine movements came the multiplying threats of a more constricted population and a chilling climate; but during this Pre-Alpine Age there was no such stress. It was a long period – about thirty-five million years – in which conditions were excellent for experiments in form; and in this respect, it resembled the halcyon days of the dinosaurs. No land-animals, except among the insects, have ever equalled the dinosaurs in the bizarre and the grotesque; but the mammals came near to them during this period of phantasy.

It would require a special study to record all the improbable animals that evolved in the first half of the Caenozoic Era. There were the Uintatheres, which grew to the size of a small elephant; they had no trunk, but three pairs of horns – one pair above the nose, another behind the eyes, and a third, rounded and probably covered with skin, on the top of their heads; and the males, in an added gesture of extravagance, had long, down-curving tusks. There were the Chalicotheres, some of which were as big as a horse; they resembled horses in certain parts, but their feet were armed with huge claws; and it was not until a complete skeleton was discovered that the skull and the feet were attributed to the same animal. As their teeth show that they were vegetarians, they probably used their claws for digging up roots. There was Baluchitherium, the hornless rhinoceros, the largest land-mammal that has ever lived, standing sixteen feet high at the shoulders. As its name implies, it roamed the country that is now Baluchistan.

Odd though they were, the way of life of these animals and of some others equally curious is at least imaginable, but – 'sometimes,' Professor Agar writes,

> even the palaeontologist's capacity for hypothesis fails, and we are left with fossil remains which are a complete ecological mystery. There are, for instance, a whole series of inexplicable mammals in the Tertiary of South America – the Astrapotheria. One of these is Astrapotherium, which was a large animal, about three metres long, with a strange truncated skull. There were no upper incisors, but very long canine teeth; the nasal openings were slit-like and placed on the top of the head; there were very strong forelimbs, but very weak hindlimbs. Romer concluded: "All in all, the creature's mode of life is beyond reasonable conjecture." '*

*D. V. Agar, *Principles of Palaeoecology*, McGraw-Hill, New York, 1963, p. 57.

Such fascinating oddities belong to an age of plenty, when life, like an Edwardian hat, goes to the limit of exuberance; but the frivolity of these zoological fashion-plates is really a minor matter, and it was offset by some serious trends. When the next period of stress set in, with the first Alpine movements towards the middle of the era, the eccentrics became extinct, and only the main trend-lines were carried on into the modern world. Outstanding among those that survived and prospered were the Primates.

PROSIMIANS AND ANTHROPOIDS

The Primates began as a group of the placental mammals that remained in the trees and preferred a warm climate. The need for warmth restricted their habitat more and more with the passing of time, because the climatic trend of the Caenozoic Era was for the north to grow colder. Their homeland was probably the sub-tropical forest bordering the Tethys; but in the early part of the era it was still warm enough for them to spread widely, and they even reached America. Later, the northern lands became less and less to their liking; and their great evolutionary advances – to the anthropoids and then to the hominids – were almost certainly made in Africa.

The Primates avoided over-specialization, which often leads to a dead-end, and they remained adaptable. They kept to the old reptilian pattern of five 'fingers' and 'toes'; they developed the free use of these digits and so acquired dexterity; they converted their claws into flattened nails covering sensitive pads; their snouts or muzzles shortened into faces; they improved their sight, but lost their keen sense of smell; and they enlarged their brains – especially the forebrain. The steady development of these trends has led to us, and in the early stages it was encouraged by an arboreal habitat. Tree-dwelling requires a firm grasp, clear sight, and a well-developed brain to co-ordinate muscular activity.

It is notable that the Primates are the only mammalian order in which there are still-living representatives of its principle stages of evolution: tree-shrews, lemurs, tarsirs, monkeys, apes, men – these flourishing animals exemplify the sequence of development as it was unfolded in time, and the trees of

146

African and Asiatic forests still shelter a population which represents them all. The reason for this is that as the Primates evolved, each successive grade found its own ecological niche among the leaves. The smallest and most primitive confined themselves mainly to the tree-tops; the medium-sized Primates lived among the larger boughs; and, finally, the most bulky of them took to the ground. This descending order is also the time-order of their evolution, and it seems the most pleasant picture that has yet been painted of the fall of man.

The tree-shrews, lemurs and tarsirs are grouped together as prosimians; the monkeys, apes and men as anthropoids. During their first thirty million years, the Primates remained at the prosimian level; then, from a population resembling the modern tarsirs, the earliest anthropoids arose. Where did this happen? All the surviving Primates – except man and a few eccentric monkeys – live in a warm climate. It is therefore reasonably certain that the anthropoid emergence took place in a tropical or sub-tropical zone; and their record, as we now have it, suggests that the place was northern Africa and the time near the middle of the Caenozoic Era. But a backward glance at the preceding era will help to clarify this significant event.

During the Great Marine Epoch, when the rocks that are now the cliffs of Dover were being laid down beneath the Great Chalk Sea, North Africa had shared the fortunes of Europe. The Tethys had then overflowed all its shores; and for a long time the Sahara, like Europe, had been an archipelago. At their greatest extent, these waters had isolated the whole north-west corner, and had joined the Gulf of Guinea; but towards the end of the era they began to recede. Then came a premonitory shudder of the Alpine movements, many millions of years before the main event, which brought emergent lands in Europe, and the Saharan Sea continued to regress. Its changing coast-line can be followed through the length of Egypt. Early in the Caenozoic it was at Assouan; but shortly before the middle of the era, about 40,000,000 B.P., it was near the Fayoum, then an estuary of the primordial Nile, and it is here that the remains of the first-known anthropoid have been discovered.

This small creature has now been saddled with a big name – Propliopithicus. His family must have emerged from a group of prosimians not unlike the modern tarsirs. Propliopithicus may not be a direct ancestor of ours; but he is certainly a chip, the earliest yet known, off the old block of monkeys, apes and men. The head of the family must have closely resembled him, and it is on the southern shores of the Tethys that we must look for our origins.

If North Africa was the centre of anthropoid radiation, this might also help to explain two other facts. The first is that somehow they reached South America, where they were cut off, and developed in isolation as the New World monkeys. No one knows how they got there, for by that time the land-connections are thought to have ceased; but the African porcupines also made this perplexing journey, and both these emigrants, as Furon remarks, *'nous donnent beaucoup de souci.'* The second fact is that the hominid line almost certainly arose in Africa, and it would therefore seem that Africa has been the main theatre of anthropoid evolution.

Although Propliopithicus has attracted more attention than any other animal then living in the Fayoum, there were others of interest. Some of them might be considered mere curiosities, whose descendants diminished and finally disappeared; but others gave rise to famous lines. One of these was Palaeo-mastodon, the ancestral elephant. At this time, he was about the size of a medium pig, with a long upper lip, the merest intimation of a trunk; but some of his descendants grew such exaggerated tusks that they had to extend the trunk in order to get food into their mouths; and so came into being a unique and versatile member, able to manipulate things with delicacy and strength. This family had many branches and most of them were great travellers – the mastodons, the woolly mammoths, and the modern elephants.

One can imagine that Propliopithicus looked down from the branches with some misgiving on the blundering Palaeo-mastodon; but even at that time, he was beginning to enjoy the advantages of hand and eye which he owed to his arboreal life. Millions of years afterwards when the paths of their families crossed again – represented then by primitive man and the woolly mammoth – the mammoth was far greater in stature and in strength, but primitive man had a weapon in his hand. This – a weapon directed by an expanded brain – marked the end of the ancient community of life, and the beginning of our specific tyranny. In consequence, the descendants of one family now sit in plush seats, while those of the other do tricks for their entertainment and are then hustled back into their cages. So the pattern has changed, in the comparatively short period of forty million years, since Propliopithicus looked down from the branches; and now the only hope that is left for the descendants of Palaeomastodon is that those of his clever little cousin may eventually blow up the circus.

It may be noted in passing that the anthropoids of South America did not press on to the hominid level of evolution. Perhaps arboreal life was too comfortable there. It may have been the vicissitudes that the African forests underwent – there were periods of desiccation when large parts of them disappeared – which provided the stimulus that drove some of the anthropoids to come down from the trees. But we must not press on too hurriedly to this new chapter in their lives. The millions of years that they lived among the branches were indispensable to the shaping of our own bodies and minds; and perhaps this was the happiest phase of our evolution – the Eden to which we regretfully look back. It lasted for a long time, but climatic changes brought it to an end. These may have been due to the Alpine orogeny; and it is to this event, which determined the geography of the modern world, that we must now turn.

THE ALPINE OROGENY

During the latter part of the Mesozoic Era, Europe had been a sub-tropical archipelago: before the end of the Caenozoic Era, it had been transformed into a mountainous, ice-covered continent. Our geophysical concepts are still inadequate to explain this stupendous metamorphosis. Its causes are only partly understood. There was a very long interval, however, between the rising of the mountains and the coming of the ice, and we have now to consider the mountains.

No range or mountain-system is ever at rest. It rises in a particular region; after some millions of years, it is largely worn away; then new earth-movements may rejuvenate the chain; and this may happen several times. Although it remains more or less in the same place, retains the same name, and may have much the same magnitude at the times of its greatest elevation, to say that it is composed of the same mountains needs qualification. The system always contains evidence of its past; but considered as scenery, it is subject to constant alteration.

This is so much at variance with our notion of the 'eternal hills' that an attempt to picture the whole orogenic process may lead to a feeling of unreality, as if it were all a theatrical effect. In a sense it is. There are hidden producers in the mantle of the Earth – convection currents it is now thought – which cause this incessant transformation of its crust. If these should result in the convergence of continental masses, something spectacular must happen along the line of impact; and this might mean the piling-up of mountains. It is also conceivable that such currents could produce forces of vertical uplift, and that a chain could be rejuvenated in this way. Geologists are not yet agreed on these questions, however, and it may be a long time before a definitive history of the Alpine orogeny is written. All that can be offered at present is a hypothetical picture in which much will eventually be changed.

No orogeny can be dated precisely, each is preceded by events that could be looked on as its beginnings; but in sketching a bold outline of the Alpine movements, it may be said that the first paroxysm occurred late in the Mesozoic Era, about eighty million years ago. This did not produce a chain of mountains, but a series of folds in the sea-bed of the Tethys. The crests of some may have emerged at the time; while the troughs between them became deeper, narrower, and, on their southern side, the direction from which the thrusts were coming, steeper. The whole geosyncline was, in fact, being narrowed. This early paroxysm was succeeded by a number of lesser ones separated by intervals of millions of years, and the most evident outcome was the emergence of islands.

The promimate cause of the orogenic drama is thus conceived as an approach of the southern to the northern land-mass. In the intervening zone, there was compression, folding, faulting, and finally a heaping-up of its sedimentary rocks. According to this hypothesis, as Holmes has graphically expressed it, 'the crustal blocks of the two forelands are regarded as having acted like the jaws of an irresistibly closing vice, underthrusting the geosyncline and so causing its sediments and floor to splay out on both sides . . . '* On this view,

*Arthur Holmes, *Principles of Physical Geology*, revised edn., Nelson 1965, p. 1113.

the Alps are the consequence of a collision of continents.

The second major phase, which created the earliest mountain-belt, began about the middle of the Caenozoic Era. This event may be pictured as a tremendous confrontation between the advancing folds and the consolidated northern foreland. It was therefore along its borders that the first mountains were piled; and in the new geography, then gradually taking shape, the emergent Alpine chain occupied approximately the position of the old Vindelician threshold. Rising out of the southern sea, the mountains drove a narrow northern sea before them. This constituted the Alpine foredeep, which filled what is now the lower Rhône Valley, the Swiss Plain, and extended far beyond to the east. For many millions of years, the Alps were thus a majestic, sea-girt island.

If we consider the Western Alps as they are today, the great bow of the mountains is found to be quadruple. There are four distinct regions between the Swiss and the Italian plains. When looked down on from the air, it may be seen that each has a structure of its own. First, rising from the Swiss Plain, which was once a part of the Alpine foredeep, there are the mountains of moderate size that border the lakes of Geneva and Thun and lie between them: these are the Prealps. Pressing close behind them, there is a line of more imposing peaks, mostly of sedimentary rock, extending in a splendid sweep from the Dents du Midi, the Blumisalp and the Jungfrau to the Titlis and still further: they are the High Calcareous Alps. They are backed by the Mont Blanc Massif and the Aar Massif, the region behind the Jungfrau, which constitute the crystalline core of the present system. Lastly, rising like a rampart out of the Italian Plain, are the Pennine Alps, crowned by Monte Rosa and the Matterhorn.

These four regions are easily distinguishable from the air today; but some fifty million years ago, a bird gliding over their present emplacement would probably have seen only a coast-line with some modest hills, and a number of long, low islands emerging from the southern sea. The coast marked a boundary at which there was a change in the materials on which the forces of compression were being exerted. North of this boundary was the foreland – the consolidated part of the old Hercynian Continent; and south of it was a belt of comparative weakness and plasticity, then covered by geosynclinal seas.

These contrasting formations responded differently under stress, and an appreciation of this difference is necessary to an understanding of the Alps.

The foundation rocks of the foreland, mainly granites, were very resistant; originally they had been sedimentary, but during the previous orogeny, they had been melted and re-set. The general term for them is crystalline. In certain places, where they had once formed the roots of the vanished Hercynian chains, they were exceptionally thick. Such regions formed great crystalline massifs: the Vosges, the Black Forest, and the Bohemian Forest are among their remnants, and it is possible that there were others further south that were overwhelmed in the Alpine 'earth-storm'. The greater part of this foreland had been a shallow sea in the Mesozoic Era, and a thick cover of sedimentary rocks had then been laid on the foundation. These upper rocks could be bent and folded under pressure; but the basement rock was more rigid and less liable to fold; and when it was compelled to yield, it often splintered into gigantic wedges that were driven over one another.

The sea-bed of the geosyncline, south of this foreland, had quite a different character. Relatively speaking, it was plastic, mobile, and locally volcanic; its sedimentary deposits were very thick, and their lower levels were subjected to so much pressure and heat that they were being metamorphosed in various ways. But the contrast to be particularly noticed is that when lateral pressure was exerted, the characteristic of the geosyncline was to yield, and that of the foreland to resist.

Compression was not steady and continuous, but rather a series of minor pushes and occasionally a tremendous thrust. The first response was a crumpling and folding of the sea-bed; but later, the folded strata not only emerged from the sea but were thrust – or slid – over the foreland. Such an advancing mass of rock is termed a nappe. At least four great nappes have been piled on one another, or intercalated, to form what are now the Pennine Alps.

The High Calcareous Alps are also composed of nappes, but their origin is different. The Pennine nappes had emerged as folds from the geosyncline and their rocks had been laid down in fairly deep water; but those of the High Calcareous Alps were originally part of the sedimentary cover of the foreland, and were folded by the break-up of its foundation. The nappes formed in this manner, which is termed foundation-folding, were eventually torn from their basement and were pushed or slid forwards, while the massifs they had formerly covered were uplifted. This explains why the peaks of the Mont Blanc chain are composed of crystalline rock, while those of the Dents du Midi and the Dents de Morcles are carved out of the sedimentary rock that once covered the Mont Blanc region.

Only the Prealps still remain to be accounted for. They are the least spectacular of the four regions, but geologically they are the most perplexing. In their present situation they are exotic – far-travelled masses foreign to the ground on which they stand. They were the last to come to rest; the rocks that underlie them are often younger that those of which they are themselves composed; and in places they have advanced over the products of their own erosion, so that their foothills stand upon their own debris. Precisely where they came from and how they journeyed have for long been controversial questions; but recent studies have shown that their rocks have affinities with those around Briancon in the French Alps, and this is now thought to be the area of their deposition. In any case, they have made a long journey, and are consequently a fine illustration of one of the great principles of Alpine building. It is natural to speak of mountains as rising or emerging – and this they certainly do; but they also advance. The Alps have moved northward and westward, out of the Tethyan Sea until they finally obliterated the ancient Alpine foredeep.

We have considered only a small portion of the mountain-front, and have no space to complete the picture; but throughout the Alpine movements, a vast area was being transformed. From France to China there was a surge of mountains. The dream-like geographies of the past were dissolving, and the familiar features of our Earth were taking shape. These movements were one related series, but they are not yet sufficiently understood for a unified description. Even the Alps, which are probably the world's most-studied mountains, hold many mysteries; and there is still a lively controversy on the nature of the forces by which they were created.*

In attempting to understand evolution, the causal sequence is from cosmic changes, through Earth-changes, to life-changes.

*See, *inter alia*, Maurice Gignoux, *Stratigraphic Geology*, Freeman & Co. 1955.

The relevant cosmic changes are seldom understood, but it is their characteristic to effect the entire planet. The Earth-changes are the geological, geographical and climatic. And the life-changes consequent upon them are those of flora, of fauna, and of minds. It is in this order that we must try to think – from stars and continents to minds.

The birth of the Alps changed the geography and the climate, and consequently the migrations and the inhabitants of the northern hemisphere. If they had not arisen, we should not be what we are. There would, no doubt, have been various hominid species; but modern man and his cultures are inseparable from the conditions imposed on life by the emergence of the Alpine-Himalayan chains. These are the first mountains in the existence of which we can participate fully. The Caledonian and Armorican ranges rise in the imagination with a remote, inaccessible splendour, 'Like the dream of a dawn of old time.' But the Alps and humanity belong together. They are encircled by our cities, a presence in our culture, and they have become part of the soul of European man.

THE GREAT MIGRATIONS

For at least twenty million years, although their altitude and sculpturing have varied, the Alps have been a tremendous presence in the European world. The great spasms of compression are thought to have ceased about twelve million years ago. They seem to have been followed by a period of reduction, which was offset, within the last two or three million years, by vertical uplift. It is from this rejuvenation that the modern Alps have been carved.

From about 12,000,000 B.P., therefore, when there was a chain equally majestic but scenically different, one may picture a long age of comparative tranquility. The ancient inland seas – of which the Black Sea, the Caspian and the Aral are remnants – were being steadily reduced. Europe remained forested, but grasslands were spreading in Northern and Central Asia. The climate was freshening, but it was still warmer than it is now. For Eurasia as a whole, it was a time of forests, lakes and steppes, temperate and generally peaceful. This was the setting of the great migrations.

The new geography that the Alpine movements had created was being matched by new forms of life, and among them were some great travellers. Early varieties of 'elephant' – descendants of Palaeomastodon – arrived in Europe for the first time. These 'elephants' wandered across the whole northern hemisphere, adapting themselves to every climate; their remains have been found in Japan, and they crossed the Bering Isthmus into North America. Less daring explorers were the anthropoids – represented especially by the 'oak-ape', Dryopithicus. They also spread widely in Eurasia; but the Bering region was evidently too cold for them, and they never reached North America. The Alpine-Himalayan ranges must have been a formidable barrier to the anthropoids; and although they edged round it in various places, they do not seem to have thrived in the north.

These two groups had set out from Africa, but there were others moving in the opposite direction. Outstanding among them were the Hipparions – the forerunners of the horses. Their name has been attached to a whole company of migrants – the Hipparion fauna. The various species in this host had evolved in different places, but they give the impression of moving together as fellow-travellers from the East. They include early forms of the rhinoceros, the camel and the gazelle; and there were a number of hunting animals living at their expense, among them the forbears of the tiger and the wolf.

The Hipparions themselves probably originated in North America. They were descendants of the 'dawn-horse', Eohippus, who was only twelve inches high and had four toes. When the Alps were rising, the 'dawn-horses' lived in Nebraska; but they took advantage of the Bering Isthmus and crossed into Asia. At this time, they still browsed on low-hanging leaves; and their earliest migrations were not a gallop across the plains, but a scamper through the glades. After the rising of the Alpine-Himalayan chains, the climate in Northern Asia grew colder and drier. The forests thinned, and wide grass-lands spread, interspersed with lakes bordered by poplars. It was a landscape that invited migration.

There was a new freedom of movement in this open world, and the 'horses' changed correspondingly. They became larger, adapted to swift running and to eating grass. Their middle toe developed into a single hoof, and their other toes became vestigial. For running, this was a perfect re-arrangement; but as it precluded almost any other use, it was also a sacrifice. It gave them speed, however, and in a few thousand years, they, and many other animals more or less in company or in pursuit, had spread from the steppes of Asia to the shores of the Atlantic.

The migration of the Hipparion fauna is among the most important events of the Caenozoic Era. It provided a new population, near ancestors of the present one, for the new environment that the mountains had created.

THE ORIGIN OF THE HOMINIDS

During the whole period of the Alpine movements a great evolution of the anthropoids was taking place; and before the end of the orogeny, they were widespread in Africa and also, on the southern side of the rising mountains, in both Europe and Asia. The monkeys branched off quite early from this common stock. When and where the next great parting came – one line leading to the apes and one to man – has been a long-debated question. It was probably in Africa. One must avoid, however, a closed mind on this subject; because some authorities still favour an Asiatic homeland, and no one doubts that important fossils remain to be discovered in Asia. The African theory of hominid origins is firmly based, however, and it will not be easily disturbed.

It was at some time during the Alpine period that this great split occurred. Originally, all the anthropoids were arboreal, but afterwards, there were tree-dwelling and ground-dwelling groups. Each of them became increasingly specialized for its own way of life, and therefore increasingly divergent from the other and from their common ancestor. Man, of course, never lived in the trees, but his smaller forerunners did. The word smaller is important; because if a large animal is to move easily among the branches, it will need specializations of arms and hands to carry its weight; and once a trend of this kind has begun, it is almost irreversible – in fact it will be likely to increase. The same principle, of course, applies if a large animal is to walk efficiently on its hind legs. Tree-arms or ground-legs – the choice had to be made when the anthropoids reached a critical size; and once it had been made, the common highway of their evolution divided.

The fossil-record of the early anthropoids is scanty, because the remains of forest-dwelling animals are most unlikely to be preserved. It is therefore remarkably fortunate that the place in which the most extensive discoveries have been made, and the period to which they relate, should both be of crucial importance. The place is the Lake Victoria region of East Africa, and the time was about 20,000,000 B.P., when the Alpine movements were active. It seems to have been in this place, and probably at about this time, that the lines leading to the modern apes on the one hand and to ourselves on the other parted. The most celebrated remains are those of Proconsul. Most authorities now place Proconsul in a line that had begun to diverge in the direction of the apes; but he must have been closely-related and similar in appearance to our common ancestor.*

Twenty million years ago, Lake Victoria did not exist; but there was then a smaller lake, or periodically flooded ground, in this locality. It is thought that the specimens of Proconsul may have been drowned in a neighbouring river, and that their remains were washed down to the lake or flooded land and silted over. Their resting place has since become an island; and in 1926 Dr Leakey began to uncover their bones. The record of Rusinga Island is now quite extensive, and other families than Proconsul are represented there. Two of these are found some millions of years afterwards in India, and it may be that India served as a secondary centre for their radiation.

The most advanced of the Lake Victorians had a brain-volume similar to that of a modern chimpanzee – about four hundred cubic centimetres. The frontal development is said to be more primitive, so perhaps they were less intelligent; but we cannot pass this point of bifurcation without taking intelligence into account. The differences between the human and the ape brains are purely quantitive: the human brain has only a different proportion between its parts and a greater development of certain areas. Their common ancestor must have possessed all these features in a simpler and more generalized

*Some geneticists now believe that the relationship between man, the gorilla and the chimpanzee is so close that their common ancestor must have lived at a much more recent date. This debate continues.

form; and what has to be presumed, from this point, is divergent specialization. This was determined by more fundamental changes in physique, for it is characteristic of brain-development that it comes after those other improvements that make possible a more varied way of life: the hominids walked erect, used their hands, and probably made tools, before they became big-headed in the manner peculiar to ourselves.

It will be seen from Maurice Wilson's reconstruction of Proconsul that he possessed the equally-proportioned limbs that are normal among mammals. He had neither the exaggerated arms of the apes nor the exaggerated legs of man, and so he is evidently close to the unspecialized ancestral stock from which both descend. It is not, of course, possible to follow either line of descent in detail. The family must have had many ramifications, a few of which prospered while others ended in extinction. It is the in-breeding group which provides the pool of genes within which mutations are shared, tested, and the valuable ones passed on; and the groups into which the Proconsul population was divided were probably quite small and based on the food-resources of a territory. The nature of the territory is one obvious determinant of evolution; and at the time of Proconsul, this part of Africa consisted of forested valleys separated by bushy grassland. A considerable part of it must therefore have formed a fringe to the forests in which all the earlier anthropoids had lived, and beyond this was open country in which lay the future of the hominids.

The importance of a fringe has been made evident before: the ancient lung-fishes in their muddy and inconstant pools lived on the fringe of the aquatic world, and were thus gradually prepared for life in a new sphere; the borders of the humid Palaeozoic forests were a testing-ground for the seed-plants; and in a similar way, it may be supposed, these African regions where dense woods thinned into scrub and grassy uplands, were the nursery of the hominids. From the point of view of their arboreal relations, these groups living on the fringe were the unlucky ones. The pressure of an expanding population had driven them to adapt themselves – reluctantly, one may be sure– to a more austere and demanding environment; and to be successful there required many changes in their way of life.

The earliest hominids were not hunters. Their ancestors had been mainly vegetarian, although, like the first placentals, they had probably added some insects to their diet. But life in more open country drove them increasingly to depend on animal food, and at the same time placed them in greater danger of themselves being eaten. When their growing intelligence suggested the use of weapons – not artefacts to begin with, but handy sticks and stones – their first application was doubtless for hunting and for defence against being hunted. This led imperceptibly to better organization, and consequently to larger communities; because when hunters work together, they can attack bigger and more formidable animals and a more numerous group can be fed. The armaments industry was no doubt the first of all industries, and its advent was part of a change that would ultimately threaten all nature. 'To the sociability, intelligence, and manipulative abilities of our primate ancestors were added the co-operative hunting activities of the social carnivore, producing a unique and potentially formidable new type of animal – the earliest hominid.'*

To advance to the level of *Homo* further changes were required. Man has been defined as a tool-making animal. And it was certainly in conjunction with his ability to manipulate things that corresponding areas developed in his brain and he became so dangerously clever; but in order to be a tool-maker, he had first to be free-handed; and to become free-handed, his ancestors had to restrict their locomotion to a single pair of feet. This made them slower than the four-footed, and less nimble than the arm-swingers; but it was to place the rest of life at the mercy of their grasping hands.

NEAR-MEN

The key-word to the last million years is 'cold'. The change in climate was made gradually and was matched by the appearance of a cold-adapted fauna – not only on land, but also in the oceans. The type-specimens of the land-animals of this time come from Villafranca d'Asti in Italy, and the period leading up to the Great Ice Age has therefore been named after this site. The Villafranchian animals are characterized by their familiarity: modern genera of horses, cattle and elephants appear for

*David Pilbeam, 'Man's Earliest Ancestors', *Science Journal*, Feb. 1976, p. 52.

the first time. And near-men, although not found in Italy, are contemporary with this company. It is possible that the genus *Homo* was also Villafranchian. In any case, nature was then pregnant with man and soon to be delivered.

The homeland of the near-men would seem to have been Africa. Remains of them were first discovered near Johannesburg in 1924. Since then, fossils of comparable type have been found in many places – notably in the region of Lake Victoria, and in Chad, Palestine and Java. The most ancient specimens are African, and Africa was probably the first centre of their diffusion. In Villafranchian times, hominids at this level of evolution – and perhaps at a higher level – were radiating widely, and thus laying the foundations of humanity in the warmer regions of the Old World.

They were short, probably dark-skinned, their noses flat and wide, and their faces snout-like. Professor Dart, who discovered them, described them as 'animal-hunting, flesh-eating, skull-cracking, bone-breaking apes'. And he named the genus accordingly 'southern ape' – Australopithicus. This is a calumny on the apes, none of which has evolved such blood-thirsty behaviour; and it should be stressed that the Australopithicines were not closely related to any ape. They were hominids, on the verge of becoming *Homo;* and Dr Leakey speaks of them aptly as 'near-men'. But what, one may ask, is a man?

There is, of course, no precise frontier between man and pre-man. If the fossil-record were perfect, there would still be no point at which it could be said, 'This animal was human, but its parents were not.' It is a question of the gradual accentuation within a group of those characteristics that we look upon as human, and this may have happened in more groups than one. But as it would be convenient to have some arbitary line of demarcation, several have been suggested. Sir Arthur Keith proposed that the criterion should be brains.

The largest-brained apes now living are the gorillas; they may sometimes have a brain-volume of six hundred and eighty cubic centimetres, but they never reach seven hundred. The smallest-brained human beings of the present day are some Australian aboriginals; they may have a brain-volume as low as eight hundred and thirty cubic centimetres, but they never fall to eight hundred. If one wished to draw a distinction along these lines, therefore, one might say that an anthropoid whose

Restoration of Archaeopteryx *(The Natural History Museum, London)*

Restoration of Proconsul Nyanzae (*The Natural History Museum, London*)

brain-volume was mid-way between these – seven hundred and fifty cubic centimetres – was just on the brink of humanity.

Such an arbitary frontier is meaningless in nature, but it may be convenient in discussion; and Sir Arthur Keith accordingly suggested this demarcation, and called it a Rubicon. *Homo* might then be defined as a Primate that walks erect, makes tools, and has a brain-volume of not less than seven hundred and fifty cubic centimetres. As the average volume of the modern European brain is about fourteen hundred cubic centimetres, the more advanced portion of humanity may be said to have doubled its brain-volume since it crossed the Rubicon – that is, during the strictly human part of evolution.

Judged by this standard, the Australopithicines fail to qualify as *Homo*. They walked erect, some made tools, and they all used them – in the sense that they battered the skulls of the baboons they hunted with unworked stones of a handy size; but their own skulls, although nearly human in shape, were sub-human in capacity; and they are accordingly classed as near-men. In 1963, however, Dr Leakey discovered the remains of some close cousins of the Australopithicines, living in the same region, who were more advanced. He classified this species as human, and named it *Homo habilis*. The Rubicon had therefore been crossed before the beginning of the Ice Age; but it is likely that *Homo* was then a very rare animal, and that the near-men most fairly represent the level of hominid evolution in the Villafranchian. Man and the ice belong together. And before considering this new genus, it is necessary to picture the extraordinary change of setting that did so much to form its mind and its culture.

DATING THE ICE AGE

Climates and shore-lines have varied greatly in the last million years, and the level of the oceans has altered by as much as three hundred feet. The main reason for this has been the forming, dissolving, and re-forming of the ice-sheets. We usually speak of the present time as the Post-Glacial Period; but it is more probable that we are living in an inter-glacial period, and that the Ice Age is not done with yet. Ice ages have been infrequent, but recurrent events, interrupting the Earth's normal equability, and their causes still seem mysterious. Like other crises in the geological drama, they are, from the point of view of life, times of tragedy and creation. Many ancient forms of specialized and peculiar beauty are obliterated, but from the robust and adaptable, some novelty is born. The novelty in this instance is ourselves. The last million years have had as their salient characteristics – ice and the human brain.

We have pictured the course of the Caenozoic Era, so far as Europe is concerned, as the gradual transformation of a sub-tropical archipelago into an ice-covered continent. The continent was completed by the building of the Alps, and by the subsequent disappearance of the Alpine foredeep and of the inland seas with which it was once linked. The European landscape must have been singularly beautiful during the age of lakes that followed; the climate was then freshening, but it was still warmer than today; and there was scarcely a hint of the glacial cataclysm that was impending. When it did come, the whole world was chilled. It may, therefore have had some extra-planetary cause; and this shiver of the Earth is an impressive reminder of the unity of things.

Although there are many theories, it has to be admitted that the primary cause of the Ice Age is still unknown. It has been plausibly suggested, however, that there may also have been secondary causes – which would account for the fact that there were peaks of cold when the ice-sheets advanced, separated by intervals of clemency when they withdrew – and that these were perturbations in the orbit of the Earth. These perturbations could not explain the main event, but it is argued that they might have occasioned the relative changes that took place within it. It was once thought that the Ice Age was continuous; but geological evidence has shown that it was not, and that there were long inter-glacial periods when the climate was not unlike the present-day.

The Earth's incessant journey round the Sun is not perfectly repetitive; the attraction of the other planets causes slight variations, and in consequence the amount of solar heat reaching any particular latitude varies over a long time-span. These variations can be calculated for the past; and when this is done for the northern latitudes that were most affected by the ice, a time-pattern of colder and warmer periods takes shape. That the glaciers did in fact advance and retreat can be shown from purely geological evidence; and the two rhythms, astronomical and geological, approximately coincide. As the astronomical rhythm can be dated, the correspondence provides a possible chronology of the Ice Age; and this would place the onset of the First Glaciation at about 600,000 B.P.*

The parts of this theory fit together so neatly that it seems almost a pity that there should be an alternative approach, also drawing on cogent evidence, which yields an entirely incompatible chronology. This depends on a study of the sediments that have gradually accumulated on the ocean-floors. A part of these sediments is composed of the shells or skeletons of very small organisms that once lived at or near the surface. Some of their species are extremely sensitive to temperature changes; and their accumulated remains on the sea-bed have built up a succession of layers in which cold-adapted and warm-adapted forms alternate. This sequence, beyond doubt, corresponds to the climatic fluctuations of the Ice Age. With drilling apparatus, it is possible to obtain 'cores' of considerable length which display the order of deposition; the relating of thickness to time is therefore the key to the chronology of climatic change. Thousands of such cores from all the oceans have now been studied; and the findings have been used by Ericson and Wollin to work out a new chronology of the Ice Age.†

Unfortunately, their estimates are completely irreconcilable with the earlier ones. The Astronomical Theory dates the beginning of the First Glaciation at about 600,000 B.P., while the Marine Theory more than doubles this figure, and suggests a date of about 1,500,000 B.P. Although the longer period is more attractive from the evolutionary point of view, the controversy is not likely to end quickly, and all that can be done at present is to state the disagreement. It is, however, only the absolute chronology that is in dispute: the rhythm of glacial and interglacial epochs is firmly established.

THE GLACIAL RHYTHM

There were four main advances of the ice, separated by intervals

*See F. E. Zeuner, *Dating the Past*, 4th. edn., Methuen 1958, chapter 5.
†David B. Ericson and Goesta Wollin, *The Deep and the Past*, Jonathan Cape 1966.

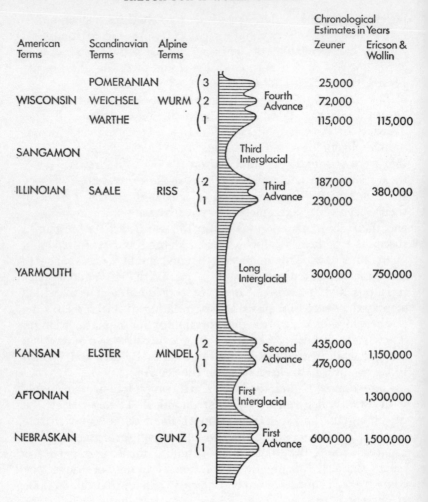

American Terms	Scandinavian Terms	Alpine Terms			Chronological Estimates in Years	
					Zeuner	Ericson & Wollin
	POMERANIAN		3		25,000	
WISCONSIN	WEICHSEL	WURM	2	Fourth Advance	72,000	
	WARTHE		1		115,000	115,000
SANGAMON				Third Interglacial		
ILLINOIAN	SAALE	RISS	2	Third Advance	187,000	380,000
			1		230,000	
YARMOUTH				Long Interglacial	300,000	750,000
KANSAN	ELSTER	MINDEL	2	Second Advance	435,000	1,150,000
			1		476,000	
AFTONIAN				First Interglacial		1,300,000
NEBRASKAN		GUNZ	2	First Advance	600,000	1,500,000
			1			

of retreat. There were also minor fluctuations, but these need not be considered in a general view. The advances fall into pairs; and the Second Interglacial Epoch, which was more than twice as long as the others stands between them. The comings and goings of the ice are geologically recorded in many places, one of which is the coast of Norfolk.

A consequence of the obliteration of the ancient Alpine foredeep was the creation of a northward flowing river, the Rhine. It built up a vast delta, far beyond the present coast-line, and made a tributary of the Thames. A channel of the Rhine–

Thames delta once edged what is now the Norfolk coast, and a great accumulation of drift-wood from its forested banks collected there. Some of this has been preserved in the lowest level of the cliffs at Cromer, which has been named accordingly the Cromer Forest Bed. These forests flourished during the First Interglacial Period, and they bear evidence to a climate similar to that of the present day.

The deposits lying immediately above the Forest Bed show a very different vegetation – one that can be matched now only in the Far North: this is known as the Arctic Plant Bed. Resting on this, and forming most of the cliff, is boulder clay, utterly devoid of plants, which was deposited by the glaciers. The cliff-face thus presents a picture, in bold indelible strokes, of the battle of the plants against the cold of an oncoming glaciation – in this case, the Second – and of the ultimate death of every living thing in the path of the moving ice.

The existence of the Forest Bed, which follows the First Glaciation, shows that the plants had been able to regain their ground after the ice-sheets had withdrawn; and such a tide of life and death ebbed and flowed four times across the northern continents. When the cold was at its greatest, eight million square miles were under ice; and in Europe, at each return of life, although the plants did come back, some species were missing. In America and Eastern Asia, there were no barriers to their southward migration, and nearly all of them could find a sanctuary. But the Alps were impassable during a glacial period, and the Mediterranean, although not absolutely so, was a formidable barrier. At each peak of cold, therefore, some of the more delicate plants were driven to this limit and exterminated; and the European flora has thus been permanently impoverished.

Tool-making animals lived in Europe during the First Interglacial, and stone implements have been found in the Cromer Forest Bed. Other tools, scarred by the pressure of the ice, that had evidently been embedded in and transported by the glaciers, have been discovered in the terminal moraines. Like the plants, these hominids were driven out; and there is no evidence that they remained anywhere in Europe during the Second Glacial Period. Were they men or near-men? As no bones have been discovered with these implements, we do not know. But it is possible that they were *Homo*, and that during the First Interglacial Europe was inhabited, sparsely no doubt, by so-called Heidelberg Man – the owner of the Mauer jaw. However this may be, the human race was certainly brought up in this hard school; and some of the harshness of its character may be due to this severity.

HOMO

We have now grown accustomed to periods of many millions of years, and it is on this scale of time that the history of our planet ought to be conceived. Our traditional way of thinking, which made a century seem long and the Stone Age virtually the dawn of life, once inevitable, is a distortion no longer to be excused. Nothing human is old, but life is ancient; and if we have begun to understand something of the poem of the Earth, our ability to do so rests upon a thousand million years of neural evolution. This is a better standard of antiquity. The human brain is the outcome of an age-long process; but it has undergone a sudden expansion, and this has endangered the whole balance of life. Our species has abruptly acquired unprecedented power over every other, and is now set to exterminate what it cannot enslave. 'In the eyes of biologists,' writes Professor Dorst, 'the history of man assumes the same importance as the great cataclysms on the geological scale.' And he adds the warning: 'Although man's technical civilization has enabled him to attain a high standard of living, the excess may prove fatal . . . Thus we seem to live in an absurd universe, because we have circumvented certain laws that govern the whole world.'* This is a new situation, but it can be understood only if it is placed in the time-perspective of the evolution of the Earth.

It now seems likely that the human level was reached before the Ice Age, but the Heidelberg jaw is the earliest European relic of an animal that was undoubtedly human. It is often termed the Mauer jaw, from the Mauer sands in which it was embedded. These sands, in the valley of the Neckar, are younger than the Cromer Forest Bed, but not

*Jean Dorst, *Before Nature Dies*, translated from the French by Constance Sherman, Collins 1970, pp. 15–18.

much younger. They date either from the end of the First Interglacial, or from a short mild period – termed an interstadial – during the Second Glaciation. Although there has been some argument on the question, the jaw is almost certainly of the same age as the sands. No tools have been found with it. And pending further discoveries it is natural to conclude that this type of man, living on a confluent of the Rhine, also made the tools of the Cromer Forest Bed, which was then a part of the Rhine Delta. The time-interval is not too great to disturb this view; and one may provisionally suppose that the whole Rhine Valley was the homeland of Heidelberg Man during at least the latter part of the First Interglacial.

To what other human forms was he related?

With the exception of *Homo habilis*, the most ancient fossils so far discovered that are recognized as human beyond dispute come from the extreme West and the extreme East – from the north-west tip of Africa and Heidelberg on the one hand, and from Java and Pekin on the other. They belong to an extinct species, but they are human. Their precise relationship is uncertain, but this distribution looks like the tips of a pair of horns with the head missing. That may be what it really is – the remains of *Homo habilis* support such a view – and in due time we may find more remnants of the head in Africa.

That discoveries should so far be restricted to these places is mainly a matter of chance. And if we assume an African origin of the hominids, as we are provisionally entitled to do, and envisage a radiation of diversifying groups, then the picture that begins to shape is that of a dispersion of bands north-eastwards and north-westwards from their original homeland. These migrants would have been impeded by the Alpine-Himalayan barrier, and would have kept to the south of it until they could edge round its extremities. There must also have been a southward radiation; but this would have had less scope, and the main tide of emergent humanity may therefore be imagined as flowing towards the mountains, lapping against their southern foothills, and edging slowly round them. The hominids who set out on this journey may have been pre-human, but they had certainly become men before they had encircled the mountains.

The first specimen to be unearthed of this early species of *Homo* was found in Java in 1891. It was then thought to be the 'missing link', and was therefore named ape-man – Pithecan-thropus. The name is irrevocable, although it does not now seem appropriate. Certainly these new animals looked some-what apelike, with heavy brow-ridges and low-vaulted skulls; but when their various attributes are considered as a whole, the stress falls decisively on man. They walked erect; they made stone implements of various kinds; and their brain-volume was well on the human side of the imaginary Rubicon – varying from about eight hundred cubic centimetres in some specimens from Java to over a thousand in some others that were found later near Peking. It is true that their facial features would have been more suggestive of the chimpanzee than of the famous profile of Dante, but our distinguished chins and noses are man's most recent acquisition.

The Pithecanthropoids had, in fact, gone much further than their name suggests. Their type certainly existed in the First Interglacial, and may have reached its zenith during the Second; but by that time the stock had diversified and given birth to the varieties by which it was eventually superseded. The Pithecanthropoid population represents a general level of human evolution to which it is convenient to give a general name, and it was not the same everywhere; but it has been remarked that the Heidelberg jaw would fit rather nicely into a Peking skull, and so the tips of the 'horns' are seen to be in vital relation.

From the evolutionary level of these dawn-men, new types arose regionally. And one might reasonably expect that the more widely they were parted geographically, the more distinctive their anatomical differences would become. But against this must be set the important principle of parallel evolution – that is to say, that the same stock, even when split up, often tends to develop its potentialities in a similar way. It may, therefore, have been quite early in the Ice Age that our existing racial patterns began to form; and the modern type, which shows wide variations, may have been reached in different areas at different times by parallel evolution from Pithecanthropoid stock. The alternative is to assume that the modern type of man – which with characteristic conceit we term *Homo sapiens* – evolved in one locality, overran the Earth, exterminating all primitive rivals, and became racially differen-tiated afterwards. This is the older view, but many anthro-pologists now think it out of date.

THE SWANSCOMBE AND THE STEINHEIM SKULLS

Any theory of human development has to accommodate a number of facts; and among these is the emergence, towards the end of the Ice Age, of two contrasting varieties of *Homo* – the still-existing type, modern man, and the Neanderthal type, which has disappeared. They are usually classed as separate species, but there are no sufficient grounds for doing so. The only definition of a species which is even moderately satisfactory is a population that can interbreed and have fertile offspring; and it is because all living human races can do this that they are considered to belong to a single species. There is no reason to suppose that Neanderthal Man and the ancestors of modern man could not interbreed; on the contrary, there is some fairly good evidence that they did. Both varieties were widespread during the Last Glacial Period, and they may represent the products of two trends or lines of specialization. Because Neanderthal Man has become extinct, one is inclined to think of him as the earlier and more primitive; but this is not necessarily so. Indeed, there is some evidence to suggest that the trend towards our own type appeared first, and that Neanderthal Man was more in the nature of an aberration.

Amid this sea of theory, there stands out a rock of fact. According to present evidence, the first man of modern type whose existence is certain – he is not quite modern, but shows the trend towards modernity clearly – lived at Swanscombe in Kent towards the end of the Long Interglacial Period, and made stone implements of the great hand-axe industry in its Acheulian phase. On the short dating, this was a quarter of a million years ago, and on the long dating, half a million. The Swanscombe cranium is in two fragments, the first was found in 1935 and the second in 1955. There is little to distinguish it from a modern one, except its thickness; and the cranial capacity of rather more than thirteen hundred cubic centimetres is about the present average. Amongst its companion bones are those of extinct species of rhinoceros and elephant – the fauna of the long, warm period which divided the Age of Ice.

Where did this modern form originate?

As Swanscombe Man lived at a time when Europe had been

enjoying a pleasant and stimulating climate for more than a hundred thousand years even on the shortest estimate, there seems no reason to look for his origins anywhere else; and so the first clear trend to modernity may have begun in Western Europe. But Dr Leakey takes a different view.* He believes that the great hand-axe industry and the modern head evolved together; and that as we can trace an unbroken development of the artefacts in Africa, we should assume a concommitant progress in skulls. This may be true. But it is not obligatory to suppose that an industry and a race are inseparable – techniques can be learnt by groups that did not invent them; and the human remains from Africa that might have clinched the matter have not passed the chemical tests for dating. The question remains open. But Dr Leakey has put forward an intriguing theory which, briefly stated, is that modern man originated in Africa, that he was the creator of the great hand-axe industry, and that his presence is indicated by its diffusion.

Whatever the arguments may be, it is incontestable that besides Swanscombe Man and his Acheulian tools, there was also in Europe during the Long Interglacial another variety of man and another type of artefact. These are represented by the Steinheim skull and the flake industry. Although an exclusive relationship between bones and stones cannot be assumed, one is naturally tempted to associate this other line of human evolution with this other great line of Stone Age implements. The last phase of the flake industry (the Mousterian) is indisputably the work of fully-developed Neanderthal Man; and the Steinheim skull, although less specialized, is generally thought to belong to an earlier member of this race. The temptation, therefore, to link the evolution of the skulls with that of the implements is considerable.

Despite the correspondences, however, there are some awkward points. When we try to follow the modern trend exclusively in bones, after one tantalizing glimpse into the past at Swanscombe, the black curtain of ignorance descends for at least a hundred thousand years. The next modern-style skull so far discovered comes from Fontéchevade in western France, and it dates from the Third Interglacial Period. It is comparable with the Swanscombe remains in all respects, but the implements found with it belong to the 'wrong' line of industrial

*See L. S. B. Leakey, *Adam's Ancestors*, 4th. edn., Methuen 1953.

evolution. They are flake tools, in an early Mousterian phase known as Tayacian, and artefacts of this kind were certainly made by Neanderthal Man. But Dr Leakey has a plausible explanation to offer – that the owner of the bones was eaten by the maker of the tools.

Man is the only cannibal among the Primates; and it is fortunate for anthropologists that he should have developed this taste, because nearly all the human remains that have been preserved from the ages before burial was customary are those of people who have been eaten. Cannibalism, to begin with, may have been a simple matter of nutrition; but with the evolution of the intellect it became exalted to the status of a rite. Most of these ancient skulls have been opened – ceremonially, perhaps – to extract the brains. At first, it is likely that brains were only a delicacy; but the gourmet was superseded by the magician, and a ceremonial eating of brains acquired deeper significance. Man's first attempts to express himself in what might be deemed a diliberately religious manner were rather sinister.

NEANDERTHAL MAN AND THE LAND OF SHADES

It was Neanderthal Man, according to Dr Leakey's suggestion, who made the flake tools and ate the former owner of the Fontéchevade skull. And there is no doubt that the two races were both living in Europe during the Third Interglacial. Neanderthal Man is always associated, and quite rightly, with the last Glacial Period; because it was he – and he only, so far as is known – who remained in Europe to face and survive the whole of it. Then, so it seems, he was exterminated by a more able variety that returned in an interval of fair weather. The Neanderthal type was not, however, confined to Europe, and comparable remains are widespread in Africa and the Middle East.

The specimen after which the race is named was discovered in 1856 in the Neanderthal near Düsseldorf. It dates from the Last Interglacial, and exhibits the type in its accentuated or 'classic' form. This is highly distinctive. The long bones are thick, the joints large, and the marks of muscle-attachment indicate greater strength than in modern man. The face is chinless, but the jaws and teeth are more massive than ours, and the eye-sockets are larger. There is a bony ridge across the brows – the supraorbital torus – which we have lost, but which the Pithecanthropoids possessed. The living apes also have this brow-ridge, but in some Neanderthal men it is even more marked than in the gorilla. The brow-ridge was surmounted, and its effect enhanced, by a receding forehead and low-vaulted skull.

This picture suggests that Neanderthal Man had accentuated certain Pithecanthropoid features which modern man gradually lost. The two, it may be supposed, were cousins; but the outcome of lines that had sharply diverged. There are no grounds for thinking that the Neanderthal type is the older; and its characteristics that look primitive to us may, in fact, be specializations. The Neanderthal brain-volume was at least equal to our own, and its average may have been greater. The modern European average is about fourteen hundred cubic centimetres, and some Neanderthal skulls exceed sixteen hundred. That would be quite sufficient for a professor of anthropology.

Neanderthal Man was the first, so far as we know, to bury his dead. The bodies are not casually disposed; they are generally placed in the same position, the knees drawn up and the head resting on them, sometimes called the foetal posture. This must have had some significance; and as objects of daily use are occasionally buried with them, it is tempting, and probably true, to construe it as belief in an after-life.

The first evidence of ritual comes also from this vanished race. It was found in the grotto of Monte Circeo in Italy. Monte Circeo is now only a promontory, but it was an island not very long ago. The dome of St Peter's cathedral is just discernible from its summit; it was a seaside resort of the ancient Romans; and it was a place of legend before the founding of Rome. This was Circe's island, where the enchantress taught Ulysses how he might visit the Land of Shades.

In 1939 a chance discovery here by workmen digging for a foundation led to the opening of a cave. It had been sealed by a landslide at the beginning of the Last Glaciation, and for a hundred thousand years its stillness had been undisturbed. On the floor of a grotto hung with stalactites there was a ring of stones which showed traces of fire, and in the centre of the circle lay a Neanderthal skull. The skull was nearly perfect on one side, but it had been shattered on the other by a succession of blows. The man had been killed, or ritually slaughtered, and afterwards decapitated. His brains had been extracted through an enlargement of the opening by which the spinal cord enters the skull. He had presumably been eaten; but the setting is ghostly and oppressive, and it does not suggest a cheerful feast. This would seem to have been the work of some primeval Circe, and a first grim dealing with the Land of Shades.

However we may choose to interpret this evidence, the Monte Circeo grotto marks a point in evolution at which something extraordinary had emerged. Using the word religion in the narrower sense, Neanderthal Man had invented one. It was not a pleasant religion, but it was fraught with immense possibilities. Why did this happen at all? The more the question is pondered, the more we seem to be faced, as on several previous occasions, with one of the mysteries of the Earth. But the fact itself is inevasible. This vanished race had arrived at a stage of thought that every succeeding society has deemed significant. It had crossed the frontier into another world.

HOMO SAPIENS SAPIENS

To classify ourselves as a separate species when our ancestors almost certainly interbred with Neanderthal Man is unwarranted, and to term it *Homo sapiens sapiens*,* while we remain ignorant of nearly everything of fundamental importance, is absurd. The appellation sounds ironic, but the conceit is in character. And it is justified to the extent that this novel animal – *Homo enigmaticus* would be a better name for it, since we are still so great a puzzle to ourselves – was certainly the most extraordinary outcome of the Ice Age.

The Last Glaciation was a long one, extending approximately from 115,000 to 22,000 B.P., and at times it was very severe. During this lengthy span, the cold was interrupted by two mild intervals or interstadials; and it is no doubt due to these fluctuations that the pattern of race-movements is very complex. From the climatic point of view, migrations into Europe were

*The duplication is to distinguish it from *Homo sapiens neanderthalensis*.

alternately invited and rebuffed, facilitated and impeded. During the first peak of cold, Neanderthal Man seems to have been the only resident; but from the first fair interval onwards, successive waves of new-comers, peoples of modern type, were disputing the possession of his frigid domain. They appear to have come from the Middle East, and the caves of Mount Carmel are among the places where there is evidence of their sojourn. In these caves, also, there are human remains which virtually prove some cross-breeding with the Neanderthal race. Passing through this region, successive colonizing groups entered Europe before the Last Glaciation ended. They fought and dispossessed one another, and some of their descendants are still here.

In 1868 a cave-shelter was discovered at Cro-Magnon in South Western France; and this site has given its name to the incoming race. In modern dress, Cro-Magnons would pass unnoticed in a contemporary crowd; it is clear, however, that they had a racial affinity with the men of Swanscombe and Fontéchevade, although the precise relationship is not known. Possibly they were descendants of these early Europeans, returning from warmer lands in which they had taken refuge from the ice.

This population arrived in Europe during an interstadial, a time when the climate was relatively mild; but it was not driven out by the last return of the cold weather. The great limestone caverns of south-western France afforded a sanctuary when the northern lands were not habitable. The culture to which these caves bear witness coincided in part with a period of extreme cold, but it also continued beyond this into a great renaissance of nature. We have already looked at one of the records of a coming glaciation in the Cromer cliffs – where the Forest Bed is overlaid by that of the arctic plants, and this is succeeded by the lifeless deposits of the ice. There are some equally clear illustrations of the return of life.

Soon after the ice retreated for the last time, peat-beds began to form in various places, and one of these was the Swiss Plain between the Jura and the Alps. By analysis of the peat at various levels, and especially of the pollen grains preserved in each, it is possible to discover the order in which the plants came back. This record may be read either as changes in the ownership of this particular ground, each group of proprietors being ousted by the next, or else as a procession of plants returning from their southern refuge, crossing this territory and travelling on to the north where many have their present homes. In this latter sense, they may be seen to replace, but not to destroy one another. They are being sorted, as it were, by climatic change – driven or coaxed to the most appropriate regions.

The first flora, after the glaciers withdrew, was treeless. Its most distinctive member was the white-flowered Dryas, which spread the earliest carpet on the thawing earth, and has given the name of the Dryas Beds to this level of the record. With the Dryas was the trailing azalea, now a circumpolar species, the bog moss and several other marsh plants. This community still exists; but it has been displaced to the Arctic, and is characteristic of that narrow strip of the Greenland coast which is snow-free in the summer.

The Dryas Beds also show traces of the prostrate willow and the dwarf birch – the first arboreal plants. As the climate became warmer, the birch grew from a shrub to a slim, elegant tree. For a time there was a birch forest, but it was dispossessed by the pines. The hazel stole into the pine-woods – at first in the undergrowth, and then as the predominant tree. The pines moved northward to their present forests, or, which is much the same as moving north, to higher altitudes on the adjacent mountains. The hazel was then challenged; but although it was reduced, it remained as part of a mixed forest with oak, elm, lime and silver fir. The last arrival was the beech; and the dominance of the beech-woods marks the establishment of the existing flora.

A succession of animals, the hunters and the hunted, matched every change; and this partially coincided with the time of the painted caves. The artists had come earlier and survived the last peak of cold, but the later phases of their art is set in the context of a great resurrection of nature. The flora and the fauna were merely returning: this art was a new thing. As astounding in its way as the rising of the Alps, it is the first clear record of a sustained and deliberate act of creation.

It is thought that man first painted himself, for some ceremonial purpose, and that the chance marks of coloured fingers on a rock, or their impression on soft clay, stirred something in his imagination. The earliest traces of his art are hands, scrawls and 'macaroni'. One may surmise that to begin with he found the same kind of satisfaction in these products of his own creation that chimpanzees experience when they have been taught to paint – the ape-artists will sometimes neglect their food rather than interrupt their picture-making – but that man, looking more intently, then saw magic. He projected something on to these markings from the depths of his own psyche, and they gradually assumed the significance of symbols. Symbolization itself, the meaningful substitution of one object for another, is instinctive; children are conversant with it naturally; and it is a part of our phylogenetic inheritance.

When we marvel at what came of this, it should be remembered that the development of cave-art, by the measure of later art-periods, took a very long time. Despite inter-tribal hostilities, it crossed the group-boundaries; and it is customary to speak of a fused culture in south-western Europe during the latter part of the Old Stone Age. This was the period of the most colourful caves.

The great majority of these paintings are of animals that were habitually eaten. That some are master-works, and must have given aesthetic satisfaction to the artist, is indubitable; and that they had a magical utility is also clear. The male member is usually erect; the female belly is often enlarged and pregnant; and the death-spot, the weapon or the mortal wound is sometimes clearly marked. These signs do not occur in all the paintings, but they are sufficiently frequent to make it certain that they relate to the magic of the hunter, and are intended to ensure the multiplication and the capture of his prey. Were they more than this?

Some writers have described them as 'sacramental', have referred to the caves as 'store-houses of the inner life', and have even compared them to Chartres. To most of us this seems exaggerated; but perhaps we have not understood, and it is possible that these people worshipped the animals they hunted. One is reminded of a text from the early Upanishads, 'Brahman is food'. But a simpler attitude towards them seems more likely; and to speak of this art as 'the first cosmology of man' is surely too grandiloquent. What it does tell us is that Stone Age man was mainly preoccupied with food and sex – to some extent with death – and with the application of magic to these problems. Ultimately, perhaps, he succumbed to a kind of self-enchantment, and mistook the emanations of his own mind for an archetypal world; but what is most significant in the age we are now discussing is the artistic activity itself and the birth of the magical idea.

The basic concept relating art to magic is simple and persistent. It is supposed that the symbolic representation establishes a link, a psychical link, between the maker and the subject; and that this can be exploited in many ways. It is evident that hunters' magic, the placing of the quarry in the hunters' power, must have been the main purpose of these earliest paintings; and as the existence of the community depended on successful hunting, one can easily understand why so much importance became attributed to them. Such art is inseparable from a rite of some kind; and from simple beginnings, perhaps, this may have evolved into a complex 'mystery' with which the survival of the group was thought to be bound up and on which its life might come to centre.

It is difficult for the modern mind not to project its own values on to these paintings, and so to misread them. Nevertheless, although there have been much greater artists, it is doubtful whether animals have ever been depicted better. They are portrayed with respect, with a sense of participation in their lives, and without the slightest trace of human condescension. The artist-hunters exploited nature, but they had not yet enslaved it. The life of the slave is always devalued, but these creatures are still felt to have the dignity of the free. Stone Age man was no doubt superstitious, but his art is evidence that he had not yet succumbed to the most comprehensive and blinding of all man's superstitions – that he himself is not a part of nature and that it was for him that the universe was made.

It would be easy, one must say again, to read too much into this art; and the religion that lies behind it must have been very far indeed from sweetness and light. Between the sorceries of Monte Circeo and those of the painted cavern of Les Trois Frères, there lies a whole glaciation; they are expressions of different varieties of man; and there has, of course, been progress in the interval. But both belong to a dark labyrinth of thought. Man seems to be groping for reassurance through an underworld of fear; and although his new mastery of art must in itself have been reassuring, his religious rites were still enacted in the entrails of the Earth and were no doubt appropriate to that setting.

It was not only the cold that drove these people underground; for some of the caves they used are nearly a mile long, and their ultimate recesses were deliberately sought out. There was no need for this; and so the threading of these tortuous passages, opening into sudden caverns roofed in darkness that their tiny lights could never penetrate, must have been matched by something in themselves and have exercised a fearful fascination.

It is by such an access, for it lies in the bowels of the mountain, that the ritual cavern of Les Trois Frères is approached. On the way to it, there are some engravings that are not pleasant – a lioness with her head battered in, a bear whose wounds spout blood – and in the cave itself there are bison transfixed with javelins. Above these is the enigmatic figure, half man, half beast, that has excited such intense curiosity. He has been called the Sorcerer, the Horned Man, the Horned God; and very likely he was all of these, since the ideas flow into one another. As sorcerer, he performs the tribal magic; as horned man, he displays the nature of the activities, the hunt, on which the tribal life depends; and as horned god, if that concept has been arrived at in this cave, he represents these things at another level – some aspect of the group-psyche unconsciously projected on to a cosmic screen. Man is revealed in his gods, and in them he discovers himself. Of the nations of later ages it might be said, 'By their gods ye shall know them.'

The idea of a god may not have arisen at Les Trois Frères, but, in any case, this cavern and Monte Circeo have something in common: they are places where two worlds meet. And henceforward, through the whole course of human history, whether we believe in it or not, a Land of Shades or a World of Light is always with us.

Is this a discovery, a creation, or a delusion?

There is still no answer that is generally agreed. In the view of the present writer, it has at times been all of these, but is essentially a discovery and a creation. This opinion is based on the findings of parapsychology, and on the belief that no one who has studied them impartially can doubt that psychical phenomena occur.* It was pointed out in an earlier chapter how the biosphere gave rise to a psychosphere, and these phenomena must be part of its content. That does not explain their real

*I have presented some of this evidence in *A Case against Jones*, James Clarke & Co. 1966.

nature, but their mere existence is disturbing to contemporary modes of thought; and this is doubtless why so many people, when they look in a certain direction, persistently close their eyes. They would prefer not to know of events that cannot be placed in their measured world, just as the former adherents of Ptolomaic astronomy were at one time determined that no extraneous noises should disturb the ordered music of their spheres. The fact remains, nevertheless, that to draw a world-picture that leaves no room for psi-phenomena, one so constructed that it rules them out, can be no more than an intellectual pastime. It may be ingenious, but it cannot be true.

After spending a lifetime in this field of enquiry, Dr Osty expressed a conclusion that most of his fellow-workers would probably accept: 'Beyond the human individualities that our senses detach from the continuity of nature, we glimpse an immense mental world subjacent to appearances in which our particular identities seem to be linked in an inconceivable collective psychic life.'*

This is a hint rather than a definition of a realm that we cannot explain. It has aspects of both horror and splendour, and our inability to understand its real character should be no cause for surprise. Evolution is unfinished. Our minds arose to meet our biological needs, they are still mainly confined to them, and it is therefore not unlikely that there are aspects of reality that lie outside our present capacity for experience. Events beyond the frontier of our restricted world slip from our grasp, fade, vanish, and there is nothing for us but a void. All that we know is like a cobweb floating in space: it has many interwoven strands that we can follow, but no ascertainable support.

CIVILIZATION AND DESTRUCTION

Man's way of life was revolutionized by the invention of agriculture. To grow food, instead of merely searching for it, made large settled communities possible, and all civilization has sprung from that. Although some hunters may have lived in small settlements at times and tended a few plants, it was from the activities of the farmer, a mere ten thousand years

*Eugène Osty, *Supernormal Faculties in Man*, Methuen 1923, p. 194.

ago, that the new pattern of living arose. Farming sprang up independently in widely-separated places – the Middle East, south-east Asia, America. We shall never know the site of the first field, but it was almost certainly in the Middle East. It may have been in the Jordan Valley, in Kurdistan, or on the Iranian Plateau. Present evidence is in favour of Southern Kurdistan where, at the incipient village site of Zawi Chemi and in the neighbouring Shanidar Cave, grinding stones have been discovered which date from about the middle of the ninth millennium B.C.* This does not necessarily mean that corn was cultivated, but it is a reasonable surmise that the momentous change from the wild to the sown took place at about this time in this locality.

Sir Arthur Keith, writing before this evidence, made a case for the Iranian Plateau as the birth-place of agriculture. In this it now seems that he was wrong; but his picture of how the transition might have occurred, irrespective of the place, is worth recalling. He assumes that the region was divided into the roaming-grounds of various communities of food-gatherers, and continues:

One of these group territories, we may presume, had a fertile area where a wild form of wheat grew, and in autumn, when the grain was ripe, the local group repaired to this area and, as is still the habit in some parts of native Australia, not only reaped the grain, but also stored it against the coming winter. We may also assume, from what is known of the mentality of the Australian aborigine, that the primitive Iranians regarded the wheat-plant as a gift of their local god – the god of the soil and of fertility – and he had to be propitiated when they robbed him of his harvest. The natural way of appeasement would be a return of some of the ripe grain to the soil. The response of the soil by the production of new plants would convince the sower that his mode of sacrifice was accepted, and so encourage him or her – most likely her – to continue and extend the practice. When a sacrifice is made by primitive man, it has to be of the best. So it is probable that the best grains were returned

*See *New Roads to Yesterday*, ed. J. R. Caldwell, Thames & Hudson 1966, p. 183.

to the soil, and thus the first stage in the improvement of wheat by cultivation was instituted. As this field of natural wheat increased in size and productivity, the local group would begin to depend on it more and more for its chief source of food. Ultimately they would anchor themselves by it, build settled abodes, and so bring into existence a village settlement.*

This is no more than an imaginative reconstruction. But about ten thousand years ago, something like it must have happened; and that primitive man's act of gratitude to nature was followed by a harvest, while the greedy exploitation of his descendants has been succeeded by a dust-bowl, are points that deserve to be considered.

It was a religious attitude to nature that prompted this rewarding act; and religion, like other expressions of life, has evolved because it was conducive to survival. There is no general agreement on how religion should be defined, but it may be thought of as a way of life and a world-picture that are intimately bound together. At its cult-centres, these things are symbolized and instilled. But as every creature with a brain and a psyche must have both of them in some form, religion thus conceived is not limited to man; and man's religion is unique only to the extent that the human brain and psyche are unique.

When religion is institutionalized, which is characteristic of its human expression, its further evolution is liable to be impeded, it becomes recalcitrant to change, and it may be gradually embalmed. In this state, it cannot fulfil its vital function; and this is one of the grave deficiencies of contemporary society. The world-picture of established religion has become out-of-date, and consequently its way of life – that is to say, its ethic – is now inadequate. This is particularly the case with regard to its attitude to nature. The monotheistic religions that spread later from the Middle East assigned to man a position of tragic isolation – cut off by doctrinal chasms from both God and nature. One dire consequence of this has been that modern western man has no morals whatsoever in respect of nature, and the ruthless exploitation that his religion sanctions may lead him make the Earth uninhabitable and himself

*Sir Arthur Keith, *A New Theory of Human Evolution*, Watts & Co. 1948, p. 284.

extinct. We need a transformation of our religious outlook: one that will recognize the spiritual unity underlying evolution and reveal a new way of life to match our new world-picture.

The activities of the early farmer, from which arose many religious observances connected with the corn-field, the olive and the vine, despite some black elements of superstition, maintained the vital pact between man and the Earth. At the same time, they laid the foundations of civilization; and from the first cultivated field, wherever it may have been, sprang cities, nations and empires.

The advantages of this are evident, but it had also some calamitous results that should not be overlooked. These are warfare and slavery. Between the primitive groups of food-gatherers there must have been frequent skirmishes and occasional exterminations. But they were too small for serious warfare; and they had, like the communities of simpler animals, an alternative to fighting – they could move apart. Hunters are mobile, but farmers and citizens are not. And when settled societies expand to the point of mutual interference, the clash cannot be averted. The outcome was sometimes federation, but more often a war of conquest. The strife of nations entailed the conflict of their gods, and thus monotheism may have arisen, as Freud believes, as the reflection of imperialism in religion.*

The ancient hunters had at least one attractive quality – or perhaps one should say that they lacked one particular vice – they enslaved neither man nor beast. Although they killed animals for food, they seem to have admired rather than despised them; and when they clashed violently with other humans, they killed them, ate them or wed them, but they never made them into slaves. This was not due to virtue, but because food-gathering cannot support a large group; and if prisoners were taken, it was only to provide a feast.

In an agricultural society, however, a prisoner is more useful as a slave, for his labour can produce far more food and other kinds of wealth than he will ever be permitted to consume. Ultimately, the slave-owner is freed from all menial work; and then he may – and often did – devote his energies to the finer structure of society. Nearly everything that we boast of in our civilization – art, science and industry – has been built up in

*See Sigmund Freud, *Moses and Monotheism*, Hogarth Press 1939, p. 36.

historic times on a foundation of slavery or its near equivalent. The time-measure of this narrative has been the eras, and a scale of centuries and decades demands a different kind of book. We shall not, therefore, trace the course of human history. Seen in our long perspective, the civilizations of the Nile, the Euphrates and the Indus, of the Greek, the Roman and the modern world, are events of a moment – castles of sand, built between the falling and the rising tide, defended for a little against the returning sea, then smoothed into oblivion.

CHAPTER SEVEN

The Great Society

THE GREAT SOCIETY

As recently as 1922, Sir Alexander Carr-Saunders, in *The Population Problem*, expressed the opinion that the origin of social organization is to be looked for in the Old Stone Age. Professor Wynne-Edwards, commenting on this in 1962, remarked that Carr-Saunders could have extended his population theory if he had realized 'that social organization goes back probably to the lower Cambrian, and is adumbrated in the Protozoa and in the plant kingdom.'* These are not the statements of a dispute between two authorities: they are the voices of two periods. In the short span of forty years, there has been a revolution in this subject; and the origins of society are now sought, not in the Stone Age, but in the ages before the fossil-record began. The perspective has thus been lengthened by a thousand million years.

Human societies are no more independent of this evolutionary background, they are no more the products of spontaneous generation, than are human bodies. Every animal genus exhibits in its species and varieties a number of variations on a special theme; and comprised in all these themes there are physical, psychological, and sociological elements. Earlier views of evolution virtually ignored the aspects of psyche and society. It is, of course, legitimate to restrict one's field of study, but not to deny the existence of what one has chosen to omit; and it has now become evident that if we are to understand why we are what we are, the earlier concepts will have to be greatly enlarged. The concrete evidence of evolution, recorded in the rocks, is mainly bones. Decades of careful work have clothed these dry bones with bodies, and countless reconstructions have made a long procession of vanished forms widely familiar. This was the right beginning; but if our aim is to understand life, we have to go beyond its physical expressions. Each of these bodies had its counterpart of mind and was a member of a society, and human minds and human societies are a part of this living stream.

*V. C. Wynne-Edwards, *Animal Dispersion in Relation to Social Behaviour*, Oliver & Boyd 1962, p. 21.

It would no doubt be proper to begin a sociological enquiry in the pre-fossiliferous ages; but in this chapter it must be limited to a few illustrations, and we may find these where we please. We are free to select any group of animals, and look on its members as exemplifying a general plan of anatomy and behaviour – a plan of life. If this original group should increase and subdivide, the descendant groups will evolve distinctive patterns which will be superimposed on the original plan. It is this principle which gives rise in the course of time to races, species, and the diversity of life. The general plan for all land-vertebrates was laid down when the earliest amphibians developed paired limbs for walking, but we shall consider here only the mammalian and the avian designs. We must attempt, however, to conceive them as a whole – as designs for living.

In the formation of a new species there are two critical events. One is a genetic mutation, which takes place in some individual and is inherited by its offspring; and this happens frequently – most often disastrously – in all forms of life. The other event is a splitting into groups, each of which constitutes a genes-pool; and this also must happen, because a steadily densifying population would starve. One or a few families may at first form such a group. If it becomes isolated, it may be termed a race; and an isolated race is a species in the making.

Since food and territory are virtually interchangeable terms, the instinct to divide into groups and to take possession of a certain roaming-ground is a matter of survival; and it is because of this imperious necessity that all animals, from the robins to the Romans, have such a strong sense of territory. Not only do they defend their own frontiers, but they normally respect those of others. As this avoids needless bloodshed and prevents the over-exploitation of resources, it is of biological advantage; and it is a pointer to much that lies ahead. Sense of territory is a constituent of the more developed sense of property; and respect for the boundary, which ensures peace and comparative security within it, is among the elements of law.

The instinct to keep together, the herd-instinct, is obvious; but the instinct to separate, which is no less important, is liable to be overlooked. When Darwin was in Uruguay, he noticed that the vast herds of cattle when feeding separated into groups of from forty to a hundred; the membership was constant, and the members discriminated between their own and other groups. 'During a stormy night,' he wrote, 'the cattle all mingle together, but next morning the group separate as before; so that each animal must know its fellows out of ten thousand others.'*

This is the first phase of a separatist movement – feeding in company and the exclusion of outsiders – and this simple observation has far-reaching implications. It links together a number of problems – the food-resources of a territory, the formation of a society, the spreading of a population to secure optimum density, and ultimately species evolution. If the food-resources of a region are over-exploited, they may never recover, and the result would be famine. Every animal species is thus faced with a problem that it must solve or die – how to regulate its numbers in relation to its habitat, and how to reduce them, when necessary, before their demands become excessive. This need is one of the causes, and perhaps the most fundamental, of a society and its conventions.

When circumstances permit, the simplest answer is group-dispersion; and in the very long term, this may mean spreading over a continent and the evolution of species adapted to each locality. But in the short term, it means that there will be neighbouring groups of the same or closely-related species, each occupying a territory that is adequate for its support. It is greatly to the advantage of every group that this situation should be maintained. When frontiers are respected, food-getting proceeds in peace; and the upshot is an assertion of the group-ownership of a certain area, and a recognition of the territorial rights of neighbours.

When territory is held in this manner by neighbouring communities, one consequence is bi-codal behaviour. Each individual must behave differently towards members of its own group and towards members of another group of the same species, and encounters will elicit sharply contrasting behaviour-patterns. An observation by Stevenson-Hamilton of the brindled gnu in South Africa will illustrate this.

I was once witness, he writes, of a most interesting episode, when the herd bull of a certain troop chased a party of invaders back on to their own ground on the other

*Charles Darwin, *Journal of a Voyage round the World*, Nelson 1890, p. 180.

side of a small stream, returning quietly to his own party so soon as his duty was done. Not the least remarkable phase of the incident was the sense of wrong-doing exhibited by the trespassers, which displayed not the smallest tendency to offer any resistance.*

Compliance with a convention here obviated a conflict; but the underlying value of such a convention is to grade the density of a population so that it does not over-exploit its habitat. The intruders knew they had overstepped a conventional boundary and accepted their expulsion. They displayed, in fact, a recognition that their neighbours were in the right and that they were in the wrong – a sense of *fas* and *nefas*. This is the foundation of morality; and the struggle of what we call conscience – the struggle between what immediate advantage impels you to do, and what group-convention has conditioned you to feel you ought not to do – begins a long way down the evolutionary ladder.

To know a territory, to explore the region and resources on which food and life depend, and to retain an idea of them is a necessity of survival. This implies the gradual creation of a world of ideas. In the psyche of each individual, therefore, some fraction of external reality must have a symbolic counterpart; and this constitutes its world-picture. We have already noticed that the essential characteristic of a religion is the intimate binding together of a world-picture and a way of life; and since the symbolic cannot fully represent the real, the value of a religion depends on whether, under the given circumstances, its world-picture and its ethic are adequate. In order to be judged adequate, it must do something more than serve the immediate interests of the individual and his group; it must also tend to preserve the whole context of living nature on which the welfare of every group finally depends.

The episode of the herd-bull and the intruders showed that compliance with a convention – in this case, the respect of a conventional frontier – served both these ends; for it averted bloodshed and it tended to preserve a territory from over-exploitation. When the value of some form of behaviour can be demonstrated, its evolution becomes comprehensible; and we may therefore wonder whether other conventions have a

*J. Stevenson-Hamilton, *Wild Life in South Africa*, Cassells 1947, p. 83.

similar value. Once the question is raised, it is easy to see that
many of them achieve at least the first object – that is to say,
they provide an alternative to fighting.

To show the teeth, to bare the claws, to shake the fist or the
rattle the sabre are often thought of as actions leading to battle;
but from the evolutionary standpoint, they are the first steps
away from it. They stand at the beginning of a series of conventional gestures and appurtenances, found to some extent in
all animal societies, by which disputes may be settled without
bloodshed. The series continues into such subtle forms of
display as the lion's mane, the plumage of the male bird of
paradise, the stag's antlers, and the colonel's uniform. These
are improvements on threatening gestures, but they serve a
similar purpose – to decide questions of status without coming
to blows.

Darwin believed that the secondary sexual characteristics
of the male had been evolved solely to impress the female; but
the observations of many naturalists have since shown that the
display of the males is primarily directed towards one another,
and that its main purpose is to decide and to maintain their
place in the social hierarchy. The late recognition of this is not
surprising. Many women have fallen in love with a uniform,
and a student of the subject might at first suppose that this was
the reason why uniforms were worn. After further research,
however, he would discover that their romantic effect was
incidental, and that they were mainly intended to establish the
wearers' status among other men, and to decide, without
recourse to violence, who shall give orders to whom. Naturalists
have made a similar discovery in studying the societies of
other species.

Out of the harsh, primary facts of existence, a system of
symbols and conventions is thus gradually created. These
become the proximate goals and determinants of individual
lives; and to understand why this process of transference and
refinement should have arisen millions of years ago in pre-
human societies is to achieve a new insight into our own
behaviour and institutions. The force that originally shaped
them was partly, but not only, the advantage of the peaceful
settlement of group affairs – an end that is attained by the
acceptance of a hierarchy established by conventions.

This is an important element in Wynne-Edwards's theory

of social behaviour. Direct competition between individuals,'
he writes,

> has gradually come to assume conventional forms, and the
> individuals are adapted or conditioned to accept as final in
> the great majority of cases decisions reached by purely
> symbolic methods. Brute force and mutual savagery among
> members of the same species have at most a residual place
> in social competition. Even threat as a conventional substi-
> tute is itself relatively crude and direct, and not infrequently
> its harsher symbols have given place to specially evolved
> and often beautiful adornments, ceremonials and music, in
> the exercise of which individuals vie together more with
> pleasure than with bitterness.*

The alternatives to strife are thus gradually converted into
the pleasures of society. This transference is to be found in all
the higher animals, but it is particularly well illustrated by the
birds. Until recently we were glumly assured that bird-song
was nothing but a biological activity, and that to suppose that
the birds took pleasure in singing was sentimentalism. But it
does not follow that because a prima donna sings mainly for
mercenary motives that she cannot enjoy the sound of her own
voice. Once an organ or an ability exists, it always has a
potential use that may be termed 'higher' than the simple need
that it arose to supply. The whole nervous system has evolved
primarily to ensure survival, but it also permits the appreciation
of the refinements of art; and the most exquisite of human joys
have thus gradually arisen out of living nature.

A generation of poets has been inhibited by the dogmas of
some animal psychologists from writing about nightingales and
larks; but they may do so again, if they wish, with a clear
conscience. The singing of birds, as Wynne-Edwards explains
it, is a social contest.

> They sing in emulation of each other with the primary
> object of being heard and recognized by their rivals,
> particularly at the purely conventional singing hours of
> dawn and dusk . . . this two-faced property of brotherhood

*V. C. Wynne-Edwards, *Animal Dispersion in Relation to Social Behaviour*,
Oliver & Boyd 1962, p. 131.

tempered with rivalry is absolutely typical of social behaviour . . . and indeed conventional competition and society are scarcely distinguishable facets of a single phenomenon.*

In conventional competition, a song is judged; each, in fact, is a tiny work of art; and it may be that the real mistake of the romantic poets was to assume it was unpremeditated.

That the establishment of a conventional hierarchy reduces mortal conflict is evident, but indirectly it also serves a wider end. It has been pointed out that the over-exploitation of resources may do irreparable harm, and consequently a rising population must be checked before, and not after, this has happened. This requires some equivalent to foresight, restraint in the midst of plenty, and social conventions, even though blindly observed, can bring this about. If an individual breaks these conventions, he may suffer no immediate penalty; but if they are collectively broken, or if they are intrinsically inadequate, the group will eventually suffer – in the first instance, it is thought, from a physiological deterioration that impairs its fertility. Should the ultimate disaster, starvation come, damage to the habitat will already have been done; and it is now believed that all the higher animals are able to limit their population-density by conventional means.

One of the many ways to achieve this is by preventing individuals who stand low in the hierarchy from breeding. In a colony of rooks, for example, only certain nest-sites are conventionally allowed; and when these have been occupied by superior rooks, if inferiors should attempt to build in unauthorized places, their nests will be torn down. All the colony enjoy feeding rights, but only some are allowed a nest-site. This is a very effective method of population control.

There are many equivalents to this. In some species the holding of a recognized earth or lair qualifies the owner as a bona fide resident, and has been compared with a ticket or a licence that confers on him other rights. This is a very large subject, and according to Wynne-Edwards the relevant literature is already 'too vast to be within the compass of one person in any reasonable time'; but its persisting theme is that conventional societies are immensely ancient, that they

*V. C. Wynne-Edwards, op. cit., p. 14.

arise primarily because the survival and welfare of every group depends on the food-resources of a territory, that if these are over-exploited they may never recover, and that the density of a population must therefore be related to this fact. To await the onset of starvation is to delay too long; but social conventions observed in times of plenty may serve as a substitute to foresight, and by conditioning the individual so to behave that the welfare of the Great Society is placed before his own self-seeking or that of a single species, they are essentially moral.

When Burns wrote the well-known lines

> I'm truly sorry man's dominion
> Has broken nature's social union

there was more cause for sorrow than he knew; for by our selfish exploitation of everything we are destroying the living context within which our own existence is set, and without which we cannot live. In *Before Nature Dies*, Professor Dorst has shown us this picture of warning and of menace:

> For millions of years before man existed, a world that was similar to or different from ours displayed its splendour. The same natural laws prevailed, distributing mountains and glaciers, steppes and forests across continents. Man appeared like a worm in a fruit, like a moth in a ball of yarn, and he has chewed his habitat while secreting theories to justify his acts.
>
> After destroying the forests and massacring the animals, civilized man has set out to violate the earth.*

By confining his morality to his own species, man has become the most immoral of all animals; and in so far as the Earth is the Great Mother, and he himself one of her children, man is a matricide. His urgent need, for his own salvation, is a conviction of this sin.

We have failed to understand ourselves and our place in nature because we have been blinded by conceit. Our virtues are real, but they are not exclusive to ourselves. In societies far older than our own, the natural activities of mating, care of

*Jean Dorst, *Before Nature Dies*, translated from the French by Constance Sherman, Collins 1970, pp. 328 and 157.

the young, and group-defence had already led to an expansion of the sense of self to include others, so that the female would give her life for her young and the male would give his life for the group; and these are the foundations of love, loyalty and self-sacrifice. When our dogs show these qualities habitually, we call them instinctive: when we ourselves display them now and then, we call them divine. And this is absolutely typical of the instinctive arrogance of man.

We are equally convinced that we are the only reasonable beings, although our simpler forerunners have been exemplifying living logic for millions of years. They had to live reasonably or die. And it is only recently in evolution that an animal has appeared, shielded by an elaborate civilization from the full impact of its surroundings, that can indulge a certain amount of unreason without immediate disaster. In this we are supreme. In the course of our brief history we have spun numerous systems of ideas – and acted on them in part – so remote from a rational correspondence with the real world that no simpler organism could have survived their entertainment.

But dispositions to behaviour – even of the most astonishing sort – are still dependant on brains. Certain patterns of nervous activity underly what all animals perceive, think and do; and this provides the physical foundation of minds and of behaviour. In all mammals the forebrain has the same structural principles; and all mammalian minds must, therefore, function in a similar way and yield subjective experience of a similar sort. But in ourselves the far larger number of cortical cells multiplies the possible number of neural patterns, and this flexibility results in the unloosening of instinctive behaviour.

This capacity to depart from the norm is a kind of freedom, but there is no guarantee that the outcome will be for the better rather than the worse. The expansion of the forebrain in man has made possible not only his genius, but also his criminality and insanity: prisons and asylums are no less symptomatic of it than is the Royal Society. Such reflections ought to temper the complacency with which nearly every student of evolution writes of the swelling of the human head; and as our behaviour becomes less instinctive, we are faced with a question, Will this relative freedom produce more madmen than sages?

Until the appearance of man, the evolution of the Great Society may surely be considered a success. But man is a far more dangerous and unpredictable animal than was the extinct tyrannosaur, and may devastate the Earth by knowledge without love. The study of life without sympathy with it leads at best to a husk of learning and at worst to disastrous results. If we are to be creators and not destroyers, we need knowledge with love, taking from the one a new world-picture and from the other a new ethic.

Index